JUST
another
SLICE

DR SHARON ZAFFARESE-DIPPOLD
with MELISSA MULHOLLAN

 ZeeT Publishing

Just Another Slice, © 2022 by Dr. Sharon Zaffarese-Dippold
Published by ZeeT Publishing LLC

Interior & Cover Design by www.formatting4U.com
Cover Artistic Drawing by Carter Dippold
Interior Artistic Drawing Marianne Fyda
Cover Photo by Jack Moreh

www.DippoldBooks.com

 ZeeT Publishing

Praise for Just Another Slice

"A must-read. I couldn't put the book down." **-Betty Wolfe**

"As a foster parent myself, this book really tugged at my heart strings. I encourage you to read Just Another Slice and see foster care through the eyes of one who lived it."

-Nan Guidi Foster Parent, Tompkins County

"A Heart Wrenching Story." **-Virginia Armstrong**

"As foster/adoptive parent, reading this account of Sarah's real-life, heartbreaking childhood in Foster Care, really drove home the reality that many children experience daily. You will feel it all with her—the isolation, fear, abuse and humiliation, but also the hope and unconditional love that Sarah finds in unexpected places. Take Sarah's hand and go on this journey with her into a world of uncertainty, a life in Foster Care."

-Christina McMinn, Foster/Adoptive Parent

"Educators are always wondering if something in a child's homelife might be having an adverse effect on a student's progress. Just Another Slice pulls back the curtain and allows one to see the emotional and physical abuses that are taking place for nine-year old Sarah which help to explain why she is a struggling, distant child. Just Another Slice will not let me look at my students again in the same way. It is an eye-opening glance at the silent screams facing children that all teachers need not negate. Just Another Slice is a powerful insight into the trauma that a child experiences and how the compassion of teachers, clergy, and others can lift a child out of the horrors they may face at home."

-Mary Beth Yahner,
3rd Grade Teacher

"Dr. Sharon Zaffarese-Dippold and Melissa Mulhollan have brought the real and raw truth of abuse while growing up in foster care. A Family Court Judge asked me one time, Bruce, are you sure the homes you are placing these children in are better than the homes they have been removed from. As a Homefinder for children entering into or continuing in the foster care system, it has been my practice to assure the homes we placed children in are safe. Such was not the case for Sarah and Curtis. This book will have you laughing one minute and crying the next. You will recognize the characters in this well written story. There will always be the unhappy, mean and nasty Donna's as well as the Derek's, and his brothers but thankfully there will also be the Daddy's, the Mrs Young, the Miss Sandy's, Pastor Scott and Lisa's. This book should be required reading for Social Workers, Teachers, CASA (Court Appointed Special Advocates) for neglected and abused children and all others who work with children regardless if it is a paid position or as a volunteer. Just Another Slice teaches you what to look out for while interacting with children. The tell-tale signs that are not always obvious. After reading this book, you may be more aware of the answers that you are not getting from the child, when you ask them questions. The non-verbal answers may tell you more than the questions they answer. One thing for certain, after reading this book, I am looking forward to another slice. Please, please, please write the sequel!"

-Bruce Sharpe Retired Homefinder for
Foster Care CASA Advocate

"I highly recommend this book, Just Another Slice, written by Sharon and Melissa, to any and all who may need some hope in their lives or for the lives of others. They have captured the reality of moments in Sharon's life that would shape her into the amazing story of victory and overcoming spirit that she carries. It is reveals the grace and mercy, as well as blessing and favor over her life, even when it was not obvious. She is such a beacon of hope as even a child, teenager, and young woman, she found her way into the life she now has. I could not be prouder of her and her choices to not be a victim, even though she easily could have."

-Pastor Scott Lowmaster,
Founder of the iMatter Foundation,
Journey Academy, Lowmaster Ministries,
and Senior Leader of Journey Church
-Lisa Lowmaster, Worship Director

This book is dedicated to

All Foster Children
&
Former Foster Care Alumni

Do not settle for a black garbage bag again.

You are WORTH so much MORE!

Jesus, thank you for being with me in the dark places.

Content/Trigger Warning

This book contains content related to violence, emotional, physical, and sexual abuse of a child, and mild language.

To the reader, after sharing my story of resiliency, strength, determination, and faith with you. We realize that some may see it as helpful, and others could find them hurtful. However, we hope that our book will become an example of encouragement for you.

If needed, please find below the following numbers for emotional support and guidance

- ❖ **National Suicide Hotline Number-** ❖ 1-800-273-8255
- ❖ **SAMHSA National Helpline for Mental Health-**
- ❖ 1-800-662-HELP (4357)
- ❖ **SAMHSA National Helpline for Substance Use-**
- ❖ 1-800-662-HELP (4357)
- ❖ **Mental Health- 211** (You can call this number for Mental
- ❖ Health assistance for yourself or if you are worried about ❖ someone else.
- ❖ **911-** If you feel like you are in a state of emergency, please call and someone to help you immediately.

My goal in sharing my story with you is to bring awareness to the degrading practice of children moving in foster care with garbage bags.

At the same time, please reach out for assistance if needed and stay safe.

The past does not define your future.

Notes

The names and locations in this book have been changed to maintain the privacy of others.

Just Another Slice has been written to depict language and thought processes that are reminiscent of a nine-year old child living in an abusive environment.

This book may not be suitable for younger readers due to the trauma experienced by the author, Dr. Sharon Zaffarese-Dippold. To ensure an accurate illustration of Dr. Dippold's home life, mild language was also used.

The young lady photographed for the cover of the book is a model and not the actual child narrator in the book.

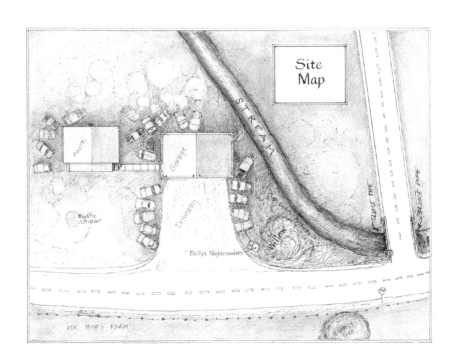

Introduction

Not one person in any of the foster homes I grew up in would expect me to have this, a *third* college degree, in my hands. None of them would expect me to earn one, let alone *three*. None of them would expect me to even *be* here.

Yet here I am.

After years of abuse, at forty-nine, I have done what no one—least of all me—could have ever imagined.

For thirty years now, I've shared my foster care story- "Anna- A Journey Through Foster Care" at national conferences, motivational speaking events, foster parent trainings, foster care agency trainings, teacher in-services, and to foster children themselves. I want all foster care alumni and foster children everywhere to know we are not defined by our past. You can still achieve whatever dream you have and become whatever you strive to be. Our foster care journey does not make us less than others—instead, it makes us fight for what we want. We use those characteristics to make our dreams and life goals happen. I tell everyone in my training and every foster child I work with, *"Foster Care Does Not Make You. You Make You."*

Through my published Doctoral Dissertation titled, "The Lived Experience of Former Foster Children Who Had To Move Their Belongings In Garbage Bags," I was able to interview women all over the United States who lived in foster care and moved with black plastic bags the way I did. The research question sought answers to, "What is the lived experience of adult women who had to move their belongings with garbage bags while living in foster care as a youth?"

Moving in garbage bags made the women in the study feel like the foster family was in a hurry to get them out, chaotic, worried, devalued, disposable, unwanted, outcast, trash, and garbage. (Zaffarese-Dippold, S.

(2016). The Lived Experience Of Former Foster Children Who Had To Move Their Belongings In Garbage Bags. Pro Quest United States Code Microform Edition. Copyright.)

Bottom line, as a foster care child, moving with garbage bags made me feel like trash.

Now, I'd like to share my foster care story with you to show that not only can you survive foster care but thrive in spite of it.

This is my story…

By the age of two, I'd already visited the ER more than fifteen times for reasons ranging from alcohol poisoning to cigarette burns all over my tiny body. No wonder I have so many unexplained health concerns now.

Many of my medical issues may stem from the drinking game "Toss the baby." Sadly, as the baby in this game, the place I landed—after having been thrown across the room toward the sofa— determined who would drink and who would not. If I never made it to the couch or bounced off, the person who threw me took a drink. I must have missed or fallen off that piece of furniture more than I landed on it.

Although, what would one expect the fate to be of a baby conceived during prostitution with her uncle being her biological father? These recollections are from what I've been told, what I've read, and what I remember, which explains why I moved seventeen times in and out of foster care. Those moves cemented my belief that there was no place for me in this world where so many others lived in real homes with loving families.

Yet here I am, the kid who missed kindergarten altogether and started school in first grade, who was labeled developmentally delayed, and who hated school, about to walk across the stage at my third college graduation to receive my doctoral degree.

As I wait for my name to be called, I smile, showing my straight teeth. My hair is styled so that my bangs are neat and out of my eyes. I look out at the audience and into the kind eyes of my wonderful husband, his face visible above the rest of the crowd. Even sitting down, you can tell he's tall. I look at my beautiful children and grandchildren, all of whom look back with such love and pride that my heart wants to burst. Such love, I have felt only a handful of times up to this point.

I have come so far since the trauma of my childhood. Perhaps in sharing my story, others can find the hope they need to carry on through their darkest days. When they are absolutely certain they cannot survive one more day in their personal hell, my story might show them that they can make all their dreams a reality.

I walk off the stage and take my seat on the lawn among the other graduates. The sun is warm on my face, and I close my eyes for a few seconds, just long enough to relish this moment in time.

The noise around me fades. I am no longer a grown woman at my graduation but a nine-year-old girl again who is about to learn for the first time, "*I am a foster child.*" And I remember…

Chapter 1
The Books & What's Going On

Whoever drops the books first should be the one punished,
but that's not how this game is played.
The last one standing with the books gets the belt.
Curtis could drop his books right away if he wanted to,
so I'd get the beating, but he never does.
He never drops them until he can't hold them any longer.

I'm alone with three of my four brothers. And I only like one of them.

Unfortunately, the one I *do* like, Curtis, is younger and smaller than me. Derek, Vinnie, and Terry—three I definitely do *not* like—have made us stand in front of the picture window in the living room.

Like always, Vinnie and Terry stand by Derek, making us play The Book Game.

It's only a little better than The Boxing Game and just one of the many ways the boys hurt us—and I'm always the one who *gets it* in this game.

"Add another one. Come on!" Terry squints his blue eyes while shouting to Derek.

We're standing with our arms out in front of us like Frankenstein with two books each stacked on top of them.

Curtis is groaning. From the look on his face, he's hurting.

My arms are—and they will hurt even worse in a second because Derek drops another book onto our stacks. That makes three for each of us.

Curtis is staring back at me with his green-gray eyes. He looks like a sad puppy that got in trouble for peeing in the house.

Curtis grunts. He's not crying, but he looks close to it. And then he

1

is. Tears are sliding down his cheeks like giant raindrops. I want to tell him to be stronger, hold it in, and not cry in front of our older brothers because saying anything *will* make it worse.

I can't stand to see Curtis in pain or crying, so I look down at my dirty legs instead. My pink shorts are browner than pink now from the mud pies I made earlier, and my shirt still has the ingredients all over it. Though making them is my favorite thing, wearing anything pink is not. I swear Mother knows it, and that's *why* she gets me pink clothing.

Curtis is moaning now. I turn, sliding my arms next to his, trying to take the heavy books from him, but Derek stops me.

"You want more books, do you, Sarah? We were just getting to that." Derek raises the next book high up in the air and drops it onto Curtis's pile.

Curtis's arms dip from the added weight, but he doesn't lower them even as he screams when a *fourth* book lands on the stack.

I'm watching Curtis struggle when I feel the heavy weight of another slam onto my arms. My eyes fill with tears until I can't see. I refuse to cry or let my arms fall even as the burning worsens. They feel tingly now like they're asleep. I try to think about all the times my arms have fallen asleep from laying on them, telling myself that this pain will not last forever.

I keep blinking my eyes fast to get rid of the tears. They *cannot* fall. My older brothers *cannot* see them.

My arms start to drop a little. Somehow, I lift them back up. These books are anything from one of our baby sister Emma's, storybooks to one of the boys' school books or even one of Daddy's books on cars—whatever they find in the house. I've daydreamed about taking every book out of here and burying them in the backyard, as Daddy did with the gray cat after getting hit by a car. It wouldn't matter, though, as I'm sure they'd just bring home more from school to use on us—and they are bigger and heavier than any we have here, so I scratched that idea a while ago.

Curtis is now full-on, crying and yelling over and over. I wish Mother and Daddy would walk in the door, but they're out somewhere with Emma. We'll hear Daddy's truck pull in and see the lights before they get out and come up the porch steps and through the door. The boys will make us quit the game before Mother and Daddy get into the house. If they only knew what happens when they leave us alone with my brothers. Mother wouldn't care, but Daddy would be so mad if he knew how they liked to hurt us. I can't say a thing, though. My brothers always warn me to keep my mouth shut, or they'll hurt Curtis. That's why I hold the books up now with all my strength. I know the punishment for Curtis if I spill my books first. He'll get hit instead of me, and I can't let Derek hurt him.

My arms shake as if I were standing outside on a snowy day. Instead, I'm standing in our living room, only... I'm not cold. I'm hot and sweating all over the place.

Derek says, "One book for you," as he adds another to Curtis's arms, "and one book for you, Sarah." Derek keeps adding them, one at a time. With a creepy smile, he sings, "Time to drop your books, Sarah, time to drop your books. Drop your damn books, Sarah!"

Please drop your books, Curtis.

"Hey ya little wimp, ya keep making all that noise like a little girl and I'll add another to your pile," Derek threatens.

I'm quiet on the outside, but on the inside, I'm screaming.

Leave him alone! Leave him alone!

In my head, I apologize to Daddy as I'm thinking all kinds of bad words right now. I promised him I wouldn't use bad words again after the day I said some in the garage when I'd dropped a tool I was handing him. It just slipped out after hearing the rest of my family talk that way. But my promise to him was not to *say* them; I never promised not to *think* them.

"Curtis, you're a little creep, ya know that, right?" Derek says, smirking as he adds another book to his pile and mine. Our punishment will be more than just the name-calling when one of us drops them.

Out of the corner of my eye, I watch Derek take off his belt and hold it in his hands. He's standing there, watching us both. Then, Derek rattles the metal buckle, that he uses to hit us. He holds the end of the belt, which gives him a good swing—and he keeps swinging faster and faster with each lash. The metal-shaped truck buckle is half the size of a peanut butter and jelly sandwich and weighs about as much as one of Daddy's Allen wrenches. The strap hurts a lot, but the buckle leaves a big, black, and blue mark when it lays into my skin. Derek's left so many marks I've lost count, and with each hit, it feels like the skin on my legs is being ripped off.

We each hold one, two, three, four, five... six books. I thought counting would distract me, but it didn't work. My arms are shaking, but Curtis's arms keep dipping down, causing the books to slide from side to side.

Finally, just as they come close to crashing to the floor, he straightens, and the books stay in place.

Any second now, one of us is going to let them fall.

Whoever drops the books first should be punished, but that's not how this game is played. Curtis could drop his stack right away if he wanted to, so I'd get the beating, it never happens that way. He never quits until he can't hold them any longer.

I look at my little brother again and nod, pleading with my eyes for him to drop his books.

Curtis puts his head down, crying even harder than before if that's possible.

Then it happens. Curtis drops his hands to his sides. The stack hits the floor with a loud *crack*, like thunder.

Curtis runs over to grab me around the waist, trying to use me as an anchor to stay in the living room, but Vinnie grabs him from behind before he can reach me.

"Vinnie, take Curtis to the laundry room and lock him inside," Derek orders.

As usual, Vinnie does exactly as he's told. The laundry room used to be a porch until Daddy enclosed it. It still has an outside doorknob, allowing Vinnie to lock Curtis in after he tosses him inside.

Though Curtis is now at the back of the house, the crying and screaming are louder than ever. He hates to be locked in a room alone. "Sarah, Sarah!" Curtis screams, hitting and scratching the door, sounding like he will claw his way out.

Now Derek's right in front of me, petting his belt like one of our cats. I'm sure he thinks I'll drop the books, but, for some reason, I hold them a little longer. I'm glad Vinnie kept Curtis from grabbing me, or I would have dropped them.

"Any minute now, and the brat is going to drop that stack of books. I feel it, Derek. Today's the day she drops 'um," Terry chants.

Vinnie nods as they all watch me, but Derek says nothing. Instead, he just stares at me.

That's it. My arms have gone to sleep. Lights out, goodnight. I can't feel them anymore, but my neck and shoulders now hurt. I must've been shrugging my shoulders to keep my arms straight. My teeth are tight, making my head and neck hurt, but I won't give in and drop these books.

Derek's face turns as red as his hair, and spit flies out of his mouth as he stands inches from my face and yells, "You cry, Sarah! Cry right now, or I'll give you something to cry about. You hear me? Cry, dammit!"

I will *not* cry. I will *not* give in and let Derek see me cry. No matter *what* happens because that's what he wants me to do. He wants to make me cry. I *won't* do it. I *won't*!

Finally, I bend down and lay the books on the floor.

Terry starts mumbling all kinds of swear words.

He thought I'd drop the books tonight, but he was wrong—and Terry doesn't like to be wrong.

The books spill over as I set them down, but I stack them neatly while staring at Derek.

His forehead is wrinkled, and his eyebrows are pushed together. His hands are in a fist in front of him. As he squeezes the leather of the belt, his knuckles turn white. He is the maddest of all my brothers now. His face is not red anymore but a dark purple. His blue eyes look as black as my mama cat's fur as he stares.

I'm scared, but I don't turn away because I will not show Derek that I'm afraid of him, no matter what. So, I just wait there for him to figure out when to punish me.

Curtis is still pounding on the door. "Let me out! Let me out! Sarah! Sarah!" He sounds so scared.

Derek grabs my arm. The feeling finally comes back, and it hurts even worse now as he drags me over to Daddy's recliner, pulling down my shorts and my undies. He pushes me, face-down, over the armrest.

Thwack!

The sound of the belt and buckle cracking against the back of my legs is as loud as Daddy's truck backfiring. The first hit stings badly. I want to cry out, but that's what Derek wants. He wants to see me in pain and beg him to stop.

When I don't make a peep after the first hit, Vinnie yells, "Beat that brat harder! Make her cry!" *Thwack!*

The belt and buckle lash across me again. It feels like he hit the exact same spot. I squeeze my eyes closed and swallow hard, but no way will I make a sound. I won't let him win and see me cry!

"Do you want me to hit you harder, Sarah? No? Then you better cry and show me it hurts. Cry!" he yells.

I think of the birds I always see outside my window and picture myself flying away with them. *I don't belong here.*

Derek hits me a third—and, thankfully, the last time.

"Hit that brat 'til she cries." Terry yells to Derek.

"Shut up stupid, what do you think will happen if Dad finds out what we did to her? If she can't walk, he will! She is Daddy's little spoiled brat."

Terry doesn't answer.

"Stand up and pull up your pants and get out of here!" Derek screams.

It's hard getting up because my legs are shaking. I stand very slowly, feeling something wet running down the back of my knees. It could be sweat, blood, or pee, but I don't look. I just pull up my clothes. It hurts when they touch my skin, but I finish and start to walk to my room without saying a word or making a sound.

Soon afterward, Vinnie walks through my room to get to the back of the house.

I hear the laundry room door open, then Curtis comes running into our room and hugs me.

As we hug, I feel his white-blond spiky hair tickling my nose.

Vinnie shoves us out of his way when he walks by us. Then closes our door as he moves into the living room.

I pat Curtis's back, "Everything will be okay."

He stops crying and hugs me harder. "I'm sorry, Sarah. I'm so sorry."

"Lie down and go to sleep. Our brothers will leave us alone for the rest of the night. Don't worry," I say, hoping to make him feel better.

He nods and climbs into his bed on the bottom bunk.

Usually, I take my time climbing into the top bunk, so it doesn't fall on Curtis because these are, basically, just two beds put on top of each other, with a skinny piece of wood between them. "Sarah, if you roll around too much at night, your bed will fall down on Curtis and kill him," Terry always tells me.

6

I know a lot of what Terry says isn't true. He likes to scare us because he's just plain mean. But looking at our beds now, I'm not sure he isn't telling the truth this time.

Tonight, I go up slowly because of the pain in my arms and butt. My legs feel like they could snap off and using my arms to pull myself up is not working out so well either. Somehow, though, I make it onto my bed. Once I lie down, I put my face on my pillow and let the tears fall. They feel warm on my face. No matter how much or how hard they hit me, I'm never gonna let them win those games and see me cry. *Never*!

That's okay, though. The boys will never know I cried. I won't let them. They might be able to hurt the outside of me, but they'll never break me on the inside. I am Sarah, and I am stronger than anyone knows…

"Sarah, git up!"

Mother's voice rips through my sleep.

I've been dreaming.

I scrunch my eyes as daylight rushes through the thin raggedy drapes on my window, then I blink.

It was a nightmare. The same one I've had since the boys made us play that game last week.

The same one I'll have until they come up with new ways to hurt us.

"Sarah, git in here this instant and bring Curtis with you."

Wait. Don't I have school today? Why didn't she wake us? What's going on here?

I hang my head down to check on Curtis in the bunk below me. He's still out like a light, even with Mother yelling.

Unbelievable.

There's a wet spot on my pillow. I must've been crying in my sleep from that stupid nightmare.

I hate The Book Game so much.

But, even more, I hate the other games the boys make us play when Mother and Daddy go out. Those games are much worse, and, on those nights, it's even harder not to cry.

And now Mother wants us in the kitchen.

What is going on?

Chapter 2
I'm Afraid & I'm a Girl

I try to hold perfectly still, but, no matter what I do,
my legs are making my whole-body shiver like I'm cold.
But I'm not cold.
I'm afraid!

Reaching up to rub my eyes, it feels like someone put glue on them last night while I was sleeping—the same glue Daddy uses in his garage. Maybe my older brothers came in here and glued my eyes shut—which is exactly something they would do. After rubbing them a little more, my fingers touch the sandy stuff stuck in the corners—ah, the crust left behind by the Sandman. That guy must have come into my room last night and put sand in my eyes to help me sleep.

Though… not really.

During Daddy's Sandman tale, I'd sucked in a deep breath and covered my face.

Daddy had squeezed my shoulder. "Don't worry, honey. It's just a story big people made up to explain to kids how the crust gets into your eyes while you sleep."

Whew! "Daddy, don't ever scare me like that again!" I'd crossed my arms.

"Sorry." Daddy had ruffled my hair. "I'll never let it happen again." He'd made an X over his heart.

"I forgive you." How could I ever stay mad at him?

"Where does that crusty stuff come from, Daddy? Why is it there? Will my eyes always do that?"

"Okay, okay." Daddy laughed while getting ready to work on a car. "I should've known better than to think you wouldn't want more answers."

He waved his hand toward the metal stool he'd bought, especially for me. "Have a seat, and I'll tell you everything you want to know."

I plopped onto that stool and asked him all my questions. Time with Daddy in the garage is my favorite because we work on cars, sing, and dance together, and no one bothers me, not even Mother.

It was in the garage with Daddy when my name changed from Stevie to Dolly.

Before I ever went to school, I played football with some of my neighborhood friends. Then, during a bathroom break in the weeds, my mouth dropped open as I watched pee come out of this tube-like thing between one friend's legs.

I pointed, "What's that?"

All the boys, except Curtis, showed me they had the same thing.

"What do you use to pee, Stevie?" I pulled my pants down to show him. "Stevie's a girl, Stevie's a girl," they all sang.

My face turned red because I was so mad, and by the time I sprinted home, hot tears were running down my cheeks.

"Daddy, Daddy!" I shouted as I hightailed it inside the garage.

He stopped welding, flipped up his hood, and shouted over the music, "What honey, are you hurt?"

"Yes, Daddy, I mean, no. I mean, I don't know," I said.

After he looked me over for a few seconds and determined I wasn't hurt, he took off most of his gear, turned down his radio, and said, "Tell me what happened."

"The boys are telling me I'm a girl. Why would they say that? I'm a boy, right? So why don't I pee from a tube like the rest of them?" I don't stop long enough for Daddy to speak. "I beat the boys at the games we play. How can I be a girl?"

He just stood there, looking at me. "Well, you are, in fact, a girl."

"No!" I shouted.

Daddy raised his hands flat in front of him. "Stop. Don't be upset about being a girl. You might be a girl, but you like things and are good at doing the same things that most boys want to do, and many times you beat them at it. That is a girl called a tomboy. That would be you."

"How can I be a girl if my name is Stevie? This has to be a mistake."

"There is something I have to tell you." Daddy takes a seat on his stool and pats his knee. As I crawl into his lap, he places his hand on my

9

back. "Your name isn't really Stevie. It's just a nickname we gave you when you were little."

"What?" I yelled louder than I ever had at Daddy.

"Your name is Sarah. We planned to tell you before you started school. To be honest, we found it cute that you called yourself a boy and let it go, but we knew you needed to know before you started school."

I was so surprised that I just kept shaking my head. "I don't like that name," I told him.

"Well, you can keep Stevie because lots of people have nicknames."

"Yeah, right, Daddy. How can a girl have a boy's name?" I jump up from his knee, placing my hands on my hips as I wait for his answer.

"Did you know that there is a popular singer in a band called Fleetwood Mac? Her name is Stevie Nicks. See? You can keep your nickname, but I have to tell you, your mother already told everyone we need to stop calling you Stevie and call you by your real name."

"I don't like that name." I stomp both my feet one at a time with my arms crossed in front of me.

"Okay, okay, how about I come up with my own special name for you? Everyone in the house will call you Sarah, and you can tell your friends to call you whatever you like."

I dropped my hands from my hips after Daddy told me this news.

"You just tell them you still want to be called Stevie after Stevie Nicks," he added.

"Well, Daddy, if I'm going to agree to this girl thing—oh, wait, I mean, tomboy thing—then maybe I should have them call me by my real name."

Daddy put his finger on his chin. "Hmm. What should I call you?" he asked himself. "I got it!" he shouted happily. "I'll call you Dolly."

"Dolly?" My eyes got big, and my hands returned to my hips. "That's worse than Sarah. I hate dolls."

"I know you do. I picked the nickname Dolly because I want you to grow up to be a strong, kind, caring woman like Miss Dolly Parton." Daddy smiled.

Just then, I heard Miss Dolly say on the radio, "Hello, I'm Dolly."

"Well, look at that! Wasn't that good timing?" Daddy pointed his thumb at the garage radio.

Once the boys found out I was a girl, they wanted to know if my real name was Stevie. I told them, "My name is Sarah." They all called me Sarah from that point on and didn't ask me to play football, baseball, or climb trees as much with them anymore. They only asked Curtis.

As I lie in bed, I smile, remembering the day I became Dolly.

Mother is making noise in the kitchen. I need to move it fast before she comes in and sees me still lying here in bed.

When I sit up, I stretch my arms over my head, my palms reaching the ceiling where there are tons of splotchy handprints. The ceiling is a strange shade of white with black spots all over it.

Sometimes, I see spiders in the corners, and I don't like them much, except for one I named Billy. He's almost like a friend, though I wasn't happy when he made his web in the corner by my bed. I couldn't sleep knowing he was that close, so I took a paper cup from the bathroom, got Billy to crawl in it, and carefully placed him on the wall on the other side of our bedroom. Later that day, a web appeared on that spot.

Our bedroom walls look like dark wood, though Daddy told me it's called dark-brown paneling. I'd written *dark-brown paneling* instead of *brown* on a first-grade color test, and the substitute teacher said it was wrong. When I told her, my daddy said that is a color, she sucked in a deep breath, rolled her eyes, then blurted out, "Then your daddy was wrong, Sarah."

"Nuh-uh, no way, no-how. No, he is not!" I'd shouted back and then walked to my seat, giving her a mean face like Mother to show her I meant business.

Just then, I hear Mother shouting at my older brother Terry. "Hurry up and get your stuff around for school, or you're gonna miss the damn bus again!" Mother likes to swear and say bad words to us, especially in the morning.

The kitchen and living room are on one side of our house, and everyone must walk through Curtis and my hallway-like bedroom to get to the bathroom. Just past the bathroom are two bedrooms and the laundry.

Everyone in my family shares a room with someone. Mother and Daddy sleep in the same room with my little sister Emma. My brothers Derek, Terry, and Vinnie share another. My second oldest brother Derek no longer goes to school because he quit a few years ago. I really wish he would move out like our older brother Travis and older sister Christy.

11

Travis moved far away, and I don't remember the last time I saw him. Mother often cries, telling Daddy, "Travis never calls or comes home."

I wish that would be Derek.

In the middle of thinking about my brothers and sisters, I hear Mother.

"Move your damn pokey ass, Vinnie!" Mother shouts, bringing me back to the sounds of the morning. Everyone is getting ready for school.

Vinnie's hogging the bathroom again using the same kind of bad words as Mother, yelling back at her as she shouts at him to get moving. "Mom!" I jump as his voice echoes through our bedroom.

"What?" she demands so loudly it sounds as if she's right outside our door instead of two rooms away in the kitchen.

"I dropped my damn comb in the toilet. Do we have another one?" The sink cabinet doors creak open and then slam shut with a loud *bang*. I swear he probably broke it as he looks everywhere for a new comb, not waiting for Mother to answer him.

"No!" Mother yells as a pan slams down on the stove.

My brother's head pops out through the bathroom door and into my room, screaming louder than before. "Mom, come on. We have to have another damn comb somewhere in this house!"

"Fish the comb out of the toilet and wash it, or make do, but ya gotta get ready for school. *Now*, Vincent Joseph." Vinnie hates when Mother calls him by his full name. Everyone in my family uses that kind of language except Daddy.

Vinnie storms through our room toward the front door, not glancing in my direction. He doesn't take the bus to school like the rest of us; he drives his car. Vinnie is sixteen. I know because Daddy says you have to be sixteen to drive a car, and Vinnie started driving one this past summer.

If I could drive, I'd just go to City Park, which looks like it would be way more fun than the place I have to go to learn—school. The kids make fun of me, and it's tough to do my work because my mind is always thinking about all kinds of stuff while my teacher, Mrs. Young, is talking. That's why I don't get what she asks me to do a lot of the time—especially when she teaches us math. Why do we have to do math anyway? I hate math. When I grow up, I will never do a single math problem. *Never!* If I could drive like Vinnie, I'd leave school before math class ever started.

Vinnie likes to wear a black jacket and put his comb in his pants' back pocket—that is, when he doesn't drop it in the toilet. "I'm the Fonzie in our school," Vinnie likes to tell everyone in the house.

"You're not *that* cool," Terry would often mouth back at him.

At fourteen, Terry is heavier than Vinnie, with big teeth like Chicklet gum sticking out in the front. He usually calls me names like Buck-toothed Beaver or just Bucky, which makes me wonder if Terry's ever looked at his own teeth in the mirror. Not only does he call me names, but if Terry is asked to wake me up in the morning, he hits me over and over with a pillow, shouting, "Wake up Bucky! This morning, like Vinnie, Terry just walks through our room and ignores me before leaving for school. Except for Travis, all my older brothers are like Mother—they're all mean, and none seem to care about me except for Curtis.

Emma, the baby in the family, only makes noises and doesn't talk, but I know she likes me because she *always* smiles when I'm around her.

Whenever I'm bored, I'll look at picture books with Emma. Our favorite one has lots of animals, and she loves it when I make sounds as I point at the pictures. Her favorite is the tiger. Emma squeals and giggles and claps her hands when I roar at her. That's another reason I know she likes me.

Now that two of my older brothers are gone, I hear Emma starting to cry. It sounds like she's in the kitchen. Emma, Mother, and I are the only girls in our house unless you count our dog, Maisy, who is very old now. My brothers don't tease Emma like they do me, but I feel bad for her because I know what's waiting for Emma when she gets older. How horrible the boys will be when she's almost nine like me. *Especially* if her teeth look like mine. Poor Emma.

While I'm in bed thinking about everything, my door slams open. Mother stands in front of me. "Didn't I already tell ya to get up and for you and your brother to git in the kitchen?" I say nothing but look down at her from the top bunk. "Well, don't just eyeball me Sarah, move your ass." Her blue eyes, with more red than white around them, glare at me as she stands there with her hand on her hip. She throws her hand up in the air, and I duck and close my eyes. Only when I hear the sound of her shoes as she walks off do I open them again. *Phew,* that was a close call.

Oh no, I wet my undies a little bit when I thought Mother would hit me. I need to get to the toilet *now*.

The mattress springs below me squeak, and Curtis goes into the bathroom. Great, Curtis takes forever in there. *Grrrr.*

I look out the window, listening for the birds. Maybe I should think about what it would be like if I could fly away from here.

I'm so afraid of what Mother will do if I have an accident.

I can't pee my pants. I just can't let it happen.

I grab my pillow to put it between my legs and take a good, long look at it. It's white with yellow stains all over it and smells horrible. I'd like to ask Mother to wash it for me, but I know better. So, instead, I use the bathroom spray on it.

I'm not sure what the yellow is, but there's always more after I cry.

My mattress doesn't look much better. I don't like to lie on the left side because it's full of holes with gross-looking yellow stuff coming out of it. So, I learned to sleep on the right side on top of my sheet.

I pull off my blanket—the one thing no one seems to want to touch or take from me. Like everything else in this house, it's old. It's covered in big pink and green squares and sometimes, I'll put my hands through the holes and wrap the rest around me. My brothers like to take Curtis's blanket. When I hear him crying that he is cold—I give him mine and deal with the holes on the mattress, covering up with my sheet.

Curtis is finally done. I slide off my bed and race for the bathroom.

Trying to be quiet on a toilet is impossible. No matter how hard I try, my pee hitting the toilet water seems to echo throughout the house.

Finally done, I stand up and freeze when I hear Mother talking loudly, and *not* to Emma. I wash my hands quickly and tiptoe back into my room. Curtis is already snoring again.

I creep over to the door of our room and slide it into the wall just far enough that I can peek out to see who Mother is talking to.

Derek.

Of all my brothers, he scares me the most. I shiver at the sight of him.

I hate when Mother and Daddy leave us with him and my other brothers when they go out. Mother isn't kind to me but being with her is better than having my brothers babysit Curtis and me. They call us names, hit us, and make us play awful games. Just thinking about it makes my stomach hurt.

Mother spots me looking at them, and I move quickly, but it's too late. I'm no longer shivering but instead shaking. Any minute now, she will storm into this room and hit me for looking out the door because I was supposed to get Curtis up and take him to the kitchen. So, I stand frozen in place, waiting to see what she is going to do to me.

I try to hold perfectly still, but my legs keep moving no matter what I do. They're making my whole-body shiver like I'm cold. But I'm not cold.

I'm afraid!

What are Derek and Mother going to do to us?

Chapter 3
Scalding Hot Water & Just Another Slice

Mother never holds my hand unless she needs to take me someplace—
so when she starts leading me to the bathroom
when it's not bath time, I know what's coming.
Scalding hot water— so hot it steams up the mirror—and my
"punishment." She always says the same thing as she shoves my hands
under hot water.
"Sarah, you're makin' me punish you this way because you're bad."

"Thanks for breakfast Ma. I gotta go." I hear Derek say before hearing the front door open and then shut. No sooner than he leaves the house, I hear a knock at the front door and footsteps pound across the floor. I remain glued with an ear to my wooden door, so I can listen to what is happening.

The front door opens again and shuts with a loud thud. "Hi Donna, sorry I'm late." "No problem. The kids are still in their room gettin' ready," Mother says to some lady whose voice I don't recognize.

As much as I want to know who just arrived at our house, hearing Mother say we are getting ready makes my feet move again. If she comes to our room a third time and sees I didn't get Curtis up yet and that we are not getting ready, I won't be as lucky as before. She *will* punish me by putting my hands in steaming hot water, by yelling or asking me if I want Daddy or her to give me a spanking. "Pick your punishment," she likes to say.

I don't like any of the choices, and I don't know which is worse. But, right now, it's time to stop "dilly-dallying," as Mother likes to say.

Curtis is still covered from head to toe in his blanket, looking like a big blue rock. He's all curled up in the middle of his mattress. There's

16

yellow stuff coming out of his bed, just like mine. I count three big holes. I shake what I think is his arm to wake him. "Mother wants us in the kitchen."

Curtis's big, round head pops out. His eyes are enormous like he's seen a ghost.

"What's going on Sarah?"

He shakes his head slowly. "We're in trouble. Mother must be mad at us and that's why we're still here instead of going to school." We've both realized the same thing.

I don't want to tell Curtis I'm afraid too, or he'll start crying. That's what he does when he's scared.

"Maybe our school's closed today," I say, looking him straight in the face. "That's why *we're* home, and the older boys aren't."

Thankfully, this seems to do the trick since Curtis nods and finally gets up.

Slowly, we walk toward our bedroom door.

I put my ear against it again, but this time with Curtis. It's hard to hear everything they're saying, with Baby Emma making noises and the lady's voice being so quiet.

I look at Curtis, "Who do you think it is?" He just shrugs.

Darn, I thought one of us would be able to figure it out.

We're more curious about our visitor than afraid now. At least we won't be alone with Derek and Mother because he left this morning.

"I look forward to seeing the children. It's been a long time," says a strange voice in the kitchen. "How are Sarah and Curtis doing in school?"

"Well, the children are children, and ya know how that goes. They could be doin' better in school. That Sarah, she doesn't like to do anythin' for me or her teacher. All she wants to do is sit in that dirty garage and watch Joseph work on cars. And well, Curtis, he does better at school than her."

Listening to them talk, I realize this woman doesn't ask about my sisters or other brothers. Mother doesn't mention them to her either; she just talks about Curtis and me.

"Ya can ask the children yourself when you see them this mornin'. I told them to get out here." Even though Mother is complaining about us not being in the kitchen yet, she sounds nice talking to this person. "No problem, Donna. I have plenty of time today."

17

"By the way, the children don't know," Mother says.

I frown. *Don't know what?* We smash our ears harder against the door but can't hear them.

Just then, I hear someone heading our way. Mother will be super mad when she sees we are still in our pajamas. I take Curtis's hand, and we step backward.

The wooden door to our room slowly slides inside the wall as it's pushed aside.

It can't be Mother because she never opens the door this way.

"Ouch," Curtis whispers. I was squeezing his hand harder than I wanted to, but neither of us let go.

Usually, Mother flings the door open so hard that part of it bounces back and closes slightly. Today, it seems to be moving in slow motion.

Mother is standing in front of us, dressed wearing lipstick, and her red hair is combed.

"Good mornin', my sweet little sleepyheads. Will ya come on out here with us?"

I don't blink while looking at the door. Okay, this person must be an alien. There's no way this woman is our mother.

No way! She's talking nice to us like she talks to this stranger.

Once the door is completely open, Mother reaches out her hand to me. I slowly walk toward her taking it without letting go of Curtis.

Mother leads us through the living room into the kitchen, like a train chugging toward this strange lady.

When we reach our destination, Mother lets go of my hand and steps away from us.

The mystery lady is sitting at the kitchen table. She seems the same age as Mother and is dressed in black pants with a white top with black glasses sitting on the tip of her nose. Her hair is all different colors—Brown with some white and even a little red. Maybe there's something wrong with mine because it's only brown, brown, and browner.

The lady looks right at me and reaches out her hand, saying, "Hello Sarah, it's nice to meet you." What does she want me to do? I stand looking at it just hanging out in the air in front of me. I don't like anyone to touch my hands because Mother always hurts them.

After doing nothing other than looking at her floating hand, Mother says. "Shake her hand, Sarah, don't be rude."

18

"Kids, this is my friend, Kate Alexander, but you can call her Mrs. A."

"Dolly, always shake hands with a squeeze—not too hard but never too soft. It shows you're strong and not afraid," Daddy told me.

But I'm afraid right now. So maybe I should shake like I'm not.

I enjoy holding Daddy's hands when we dance together in the garage and when he teaches me how to use tools. He never hurts me, but Mother is a whole other story. Mother never holds mine unless she needs to lead me someplace—so when she starts leading me to the bathroom when it's not bath time, I know what's coming. Scalding hot water.

Mrs. A. shakes my hand, and I shake hers just like Daddy taught me.

"You have a firm handshake for such a little girl."

I'm not happy with Mrs. A. calling me a little girl because I am a tomboy. But I smile, thinking about how happy Daddy will be that I did it right.

When our hands stop moving up and down, she sets her eyes on Curtis, who is staring at the floor. She reaches out to shake his too, but Curtis does nothing.

"Curtis is a little shy," I say. I don't want her upset with him since, he won't shake her hand or even look up at her.

She smiles. "That's just fine, honey. Maybe Curtis and I can try the next time I see you two."

Why are we even seeing Mrs. A. today, and why will we see her again?

After Mother gives Emma Cheerios and a sippy cup, she places cereal and a slice of toast at our table settings. "Come, kids, have a seat. You must be hungry."

I am Starvin' Marvin this morning, so we jump in our seats and dive into the food. I reach for my toast first because it's my favorite. Even though I hate mushy cereal, mine will have to wait.

Mrs. A. starts talking again, and I'm glad it's to Mother and not me, so I don't have to stop eating. Mrs. A. says to Mother, "I cannot believe how much they've grown." This seems like a silly thing to say. How would she know how much we have grown if I've never seen her before? I thought we were meeting her for the first time today.

Then Mrs. A. says the silliest thing of all. "Curtis looks just like his daddy."

I started eating my cereal by then and what she says makes my mouth drop. The cereal and milk almost spill out, but I catch it in time, slurping it back up and wiping my lips off on my arm. She should put her glasses up to her eyes instead of on the tip of her nose because Daddy doesn't have white-blond spiky hair, Dumbo ears, and light, white skin like Curtis. Daddy has dark hair, which he combs flat and to the side of his head, and he has long sideburns like Elvis. And he's not small like Curtis. I asked him once how tall he was.

"Dolly, I'm six feet, three inches tall."

He seems like a giant to me, with gigantic hands and feet. When he dances with me, he puts my feet on his, and we move around in circles. My foot doesn't even cover half of his boot. He's the reason I love music and dancing. He's always humming or singing while working on cars in his body shop. I especially like listening to him play his guitar.

So, Curtis does *not* look like "his daddy." Curtis has those light green-gray eyes; Daddy's are bright blue, and his pointy nose hits my cheek when he kisses me. Curtis's chin is round, and his nose is small like our kitty's. Daddy's skin is darker, too, and, like mine, it gets darker in the summer because of the sun. The boys call Curtis a ghost because they say his skin is really white. So, this Mrs. A. lady has it all wrong. *I* look the most like Daddy.

Then Mrs. A. looks at me and says, "Sarah is definitely a Hunter and not a Bailey." *What?*

I stopped chewing my cereal and let it sit in my mouth, even more confused now. I know what a hunter is from Emma's *Bambi* book. Hunters kill animals. Why does this woman think I would do such a thing? I want to yell at Mrs. A., but I just finish chewing my cereal, swallow it, and stay quiet because Mother will hit me later if I say anything. Bailey is my last name. I don't know what a Bailey does, but I'd rather be one of those than a hunter.

The worst thing happens next. Mother nods, agreeing with Mrs. A., even though she knows how much I love animals.

I frown and cross my arms over my chest, listening to them talk about Curtis and Daddy looking alike and me being a hunter. I don't understand any of it.

I finish my breakfast. Curtis is still eating, but there's not much food left in front of him now.

Emma has finished her Cheerios and is getting wiggly, so Mother gives her a toy to keep her busy.

Sitting quietly is the only thing I can do with Mrs. A. still at the table gawking at us.

Finally, as Mrs. A. stands up to leave, she says, "Well, Donna, I must really be going. It was so nice for you to offer me coffee and a chance to see the children." Suddenly I don't want Mrs. A. to go. Mother was so much nicer this morning with her here. She follows Mrs. A. to the front door. Just as Mrs. A. reaches out to grab the knob, she turns to Curtis and me, "Do you like it here?"

The question rolls around in my brain. *Do you like it here?*

For a second, I just sit there, hearing the question again. *Do you like it here?*

I'm confused.

Slowly, I look at Mother, who's in a trance glaring at me.

I swallow hard. The room is quiet as Mrs. A. watches me as well. Curtis, doesn't appear to follow the conversation at all—but I know better. He's heard every word.

He picks up his bowl to drink the milk left in it. He says nothing, so it's up to me to answer her.

What am I supposed to say?

Do I like my house? Do I like my bed, or… do I like my family? My Mother? All my brothers? What they do to us?

There's so much I want to tell her. I want to open my mouth and yell and keep yelling. The boys are mean to Curtis and me! They call us names, make us play book games, and box each other. They lock Curtis in the laundry room and shoot us with BB guns! And Mother puts my hands under hot water, and she doesn't even like me!

But I know better. Mother will take me into the bathroom one hundred percent if I say anything, and I will see the scalding-hot water fog up the mirror. Or something worse will happen. So instead of telling the truth, I look at Mrs. A. and nod while my curls bounce around my face, covering my eyes. She uses this moment to walk back over to me, touching my hair and then tucking it behind my ears.

Then, just like that, she turns and walks out of the kitchen and through the front door, yelling back to Mother, "Goodbye, Donna. Stay in touch." *What a weird morning.*

Curtis finishes his last drops of milk from his cereal bowl and slowly sets it down.

It's still quiet as Mother comes back to the kitchen, except for Emma banging her toy on her tray and making baby talk.

I stare at Mother as she sits at the table.

She glares back.

Curtis is slowly chewing on the crust of his toast.

I lick my lips and take a breath. Then another. Finally, blurting out in a quick rush, I ask, "Mother, could I have just another slice of toast?" Our eyes lock together.

I wait for her answer.

Mother doesn't answer. Instead, she looks right at me as she takes a cigarette from the pack, puts it between her lips, and lights it with her lighter that looks like a gun.

She sucks in her breath, making the end of her cigarette glow and crackle. Then she blows the smoke out of her mouth, filling up the kitchen like a cloud that dropped from the sky.

Curtis fidgets with his hands on the table. His eyes are on them and nothing else.

I watch them, too. Fidget, fidget, fidget. I want to yell at him to look up and say something because I feel so alone, even with him right next to me. I want Curtis to ask Mother for more toast, too. I know he's still hungry, but he never asks for more food. Why is it always me? If we both asked for more, then maybe, just maybe, our chances would be better. Why is he so afraid? I'm protective of Curtis, but sometimes he makes me mad when he won't speak up and say what he wants.

I sit there wondering what to do except look around. An archway separates the living room from the kitchen, but there's not a lot of space. So, when I walk into the kitchen, I almost run into the wooden table.

Daddy sits at the "head of the table," as he calls it, right in front of the window. Derek likes to sit in Daddy's spot when he's too busy in the garage to come in for dinner. "If I'm right in the middle of a paint job, I can't just stop what I'm doing," Daddy's told Mother before when she got mad about him missing supper.

Finally, after what feels like hours, Mother finishes her cigarette.

Then she goes over to the sink, wets a paper towel, and cleans up Emma and her tray.

She never answered my question. So, why do I bother to ask? She was so different this morning. She even held my hand without hurting me. But, as soon as Mrs. A. left, she's gone right back to mean old Mother.

She removes Emma's bib, gets her out of the highchair, and walks her toward the back of the house. But before she disappears from sight, she tells us, "Ya had a late breakfast, so ya can git outside and play 'til it's time for supper, but ya best be on time tonight."

"Why?" I ask, feeling brave with Mother across the room and Emma in her arms.

"Geez, Sarah, why the hell does it matter?"

She ignored my question about having more toast. I wonder if she will forget me again.

I sit and wait for an answer. Mother says nothing about the toast but instead tells me,

"Your father and I are goin' on our monthly run to the grocery store so we can feed all of ya."

"Is Derek watching us tonight?"

"Of course, he is. Who the hell else would watch you heathens?"

I'd been hungry only a few minutes ago, but now the slice of toast and mushy cereal in my stomach feels like one of the rocks by the sluice pipe in my gut.

I don't want another slice of toast now.

I need to get ready for whatever game the boys will play with us tonight.

Chapter 4
I Won't Do It & She's Screaming

I stand there with my gloves at my sides and step closer to Curtis.
"Hit me in the face," I tell him as quietly as possible,
so the boys don't hear me.
He shakes his head no and begins to cry.
"Hit me in the face," I tell him with my voice getting louder.
"No, Sarah, I won't do it."

"Let's go to the creek, Sarah." *Now* Curtis decides to talk.

I shake my head but then realize it's a great idea. "Okay, let's go."

He's out the door before I can move away from the table, racing me without saying we're having a contest. He slips on his shoes and runs down the porch steps.

When I get to the porch, I skip putting mine on. I hate wearing them and would go barefoot all the time. Mother always yells at me for going without shoes, probably because my feet are always dirty, and I drag mud into the house. It's not the same for Curtis, as he always wears shoes.

Everything we do turns into a contest. When we climb trees, I can climb higher and faster—when we have spitting contests, I spit the farthest. I'm the oldest, bigger than Curtis, so I *should* be better at most things. But it still makes Curtis mad.

When we need to get away from our older brothers or Mother, we always go to the creek and our sluice pipe fort. The small stream runs through the sluice pipe and along the road past the garage. It's been our special place for as long as I can remember.

There are two ways to get to the sluice. First, down the bank next to the garage. Then, we walk up the stream stepping from one rock to another that Curtis and I made as a path. Or we can turn left at the end of the driveway onto the road. We take a hundred steps, then turn left by the walnut tree to head down the bank of pricker bushes into the creek. Once we're in the water, we have to walk about twenty steps to get to the rocks we climb to get into the sluice pipe.

We do have to be careful, though, because the bottom of the stream can be slimy, making it easy for us to fall on our bums. The water is so clear we can see the bottom making it easy to have our minnow- catching contests.

Curtis wins every minnow-catching contest we have. I have no idea how he does it. It's like he calls them to him or something. No matter how much I practice, I always end the day with less than him. It's the same deal with rock-skipping. Because the water isn't very deep in most parts of the creek, they don't go far when we throw them. Though Curtis can get his to skip twice before hitting the bank. I barely make one.

"Curtis, why do you think Mrs. A. said you look like Daddy?" "I don't know. She must need new glasses. Or maybe she's just old Sarah." My stomach starts to hurt from laughing so hard. "Yup, Curtis, you're right. She needs to get better glasses to see the difference between you and Daddy," I make a funny face trying to look like Mrs. A. "Sarah, stop!" Curtis steps onto a slimy rock, slipping and falling into the creek. He is now sitting on his bum in the water, soaking wet. As I walk forward to point and laugh at Curtis, I slip on the mud and lose my balance. Just like that, I am sitting in the water next to him. Before long, we are splashing each other.

We spend the rest of this day playing in the stream. We make sure to dry off before we go home, so we don't get in trouble with Mother. I forget all about our older brothers watching us tonight until I notice the location of the sun in the sky. "We've got to go. It's time for dinner, Curtis." I'm hungry since we didn't have lunch, but I don't want to go home either.

As soon as we get inside, I smell it. My least favorite meal. Stuffed peppers. Double yuck. Maisy will be eating dog food and stuffed peppers tonight as she curls up by my feet under the table, and I drop pieces down to her. And I will be hungry again. But I probably won't be able to eat much anyway. My stomach does a somersault whenever I imagine what awful game Derek will come up with for us to play tonight.

After dinner, Mother says, "Listen up, Sarah, ya better behave for

Derek and do what he tells you and Curtis to do. I don't want to hear ya give him any crap, ya hear?" "Okay," is all I say to Mother before she and Daddy head for the door. Before walking out, Daddy stops and turns around to blow me a kiss.

Then, they're gone.

I am rooted to this spot on the floor like a tree when Derek appears with red boxing gloves from the back of the house. He holds them out in front of him.

He wants us to put them on.

"No, I won't do it!" I yell at Derek. "You can't make me!"

"You need to pipe down and calm your ass right now. You'll do it… or I will." Though my other two brothers are here, Derek's the game-maker in this family. He always tells us what to do while we "play." Terry and Vinnie just follow Derek's orders like the puppets at my school. Derek shoves the gloves at me. "And if *I'm* the one to do it, I promise you, I will hurt him worse than you ever could."

"What's it going to be, Bucky?" Terry sings out. "Are you going to punch Curtis in the face, or will Derek have to do it for you?"

I say nothing, knowing Vinnie hopes that Derek will get to punch Curtis instead of me.

Curtis and I slip our hands into the gloves and then face each other.

I look at him with tears in my eyes.

The rules of The Boxing Game are simple—we hit each other with these awful gloves until Derek tells us we can stop or until one of us bleeds. Oh, how I hate this game! 'Course, there aren't *any* games that the boys make us play that I actually like. But, honestly? The Book Game is better than The Boxing Game.

"I want to play The Book Game instead," I tell Derek. At least when we play that game, I can protect Curtis.

"Nope. It's boxing night at the Connor house," he says with a crooked smile. "You mean the Bailey house," I correct Derek. "No stupid, this is the Connor house," Terry announces.

Why is my last name and Curtis's last name Bailey if everyone else is a Connor?

I scowl, but I need to concentrate on this game right now. I have to figure out how to protect Curtis and end the game quickly.

The only way I can do that when we play this game is to get Curtis to hit me. So, tonight, I decide to have him hit me in the nose until it bleeds. Then the game will be over. Yup, that's what I'll do.

Derek yells, "Go!" and then stands back, grinning. Vinnie and Terry yell at us to punch each other.

My gloves are at my side as I step closer to Curtis. "Hit me in the face," I tell him as quietly as possible, so the boys don't hear me.

He shakes his head no and begins to cry.

"Hit me in the face," I say louder.

"No, Sarah, I won't do it."

"Curtis, hit me in the nose!" I shout so loud it hurts my throat.

Derek starts laughing. "If one of you don't hit the other pretty soon, I'll step in and hit ya both!" He faces me, still grinning. "You can sit there and watch me pound your wimp of a brother first, Sarah, before I hit you. I promise it'll be a great show."

I squeeze my eyes shut. *Think, Sarah. Think fast.* How can I end this game? I can't let Derek touch Curtis.

I punch Curtis in the arm a few times to get him mad enough to hit me.

"Hit me in the face, Curtis." I punch his arm.

He doesn't move.

My plan isn't working.

"C'mon, Curtis, punch me!" I punch his arm again.

He still doesn't move.

"Curtis! You *have* to punch me!"

"I won't do it, Sarah. No!" He keeps his hands at his sides.

I punch him some more in his arm. I don't want to hurt him, but Derek will hurt him if he doesn't do something soon. Doesn't he know I'm trying to help him?

"Curtis, please. Just punch me." I'm begging him now. Tears are filling my eyes. Of course, I won't cry. Derek will *never* see me cry.

But Derek doesn't just want me to cry; he wants blood.

And then I remember—Curtis's lip got split when he wrecked his bike a few days ago.

I punch him in the lip—just hard enough to make him bleed, but not enough to really hurt him.

"Ow!" Curtis's lip starts bleeding, and it runs down his chin. He swipes at it, which only smears more blood.

Exactly what I'd wanted, but I didn't want to hurt him.

Derek starts waving his arms. "Stop the fight! We have a winner!" *I hate him. I hate him. I hate him*, I think as he takes off our gloves. "Stop crying, you baby!" Vinnie shouts at Curtis.

Terry laughs, pointing at Curtis. "I'd cry, too, if my sister just kicked my ass."

"Shut up and stop crying or I'll give you something to cry about! Both of you, get back to your bedroom and don't come out! I don't want to see either of you again for the rest of the night. And, if you tell Mom or Dad about this game, you know what'll happen."

Curtis rushes through our room and into the bathroom.

Before Derek is off the porch, he yells back inside to Vinnie, "Close their door!"

I head into my room, making it right before Vinnie slams the door closed. Good. I don't want to be with them anymore tonight anyway. Curtis is in the bathroom, putting wet toilet paper on his lip.

I blink back tears. "I'm sorry. I didn't want to do it. I was trying to keep Derek from hitting you, is all. I never want to hurt you. The next time we play this game, please hit me in the nose so it will bleed, okay?"

Curtis's eyes are so full of tears. When he finally speaks, they spill out just like water pouring out of the sluice pipe. "I won't ever hit you, Sarah."

I don't say anything because I'll cry, too, if I do.

"I'm glad *you* hit me instead of Derek. He doesn't stop once he starts."

I just nod and try to smile. I love my little brother so much. I always try to protect him.

Always.

"Let's just go to bed, Curtis. I'm tired.".

"Me, too." I agree with him, even though my sleep will be filled with nightmares. Maybe If I force myself to stay awake, I can stop them. If only it was that easy in real life.

The next morning, I wake up to Mother yelling. That's normal, but what *isn't* normal is that she's in the bathroom yelling to Daddy, flushing the toilet over and over.

Baby Emma starts to cry, and Daddy runs in, "Joseph!" Mother shrieks, "when I sat on this damn toilet, I felt somethin' hittin' my ass.

Then, when I stood up, I saw a damn mouse in there! How the *hell* did a damn mouse get in the damn toilet?"

"Well, Donna, it's not a mouse. It's a rat. I would guess it swam up the plumbing somehow or was able to get into the pipe," Daddy says in a calm voice like it's no big deal.

"A *rat*? That's even worse! Well, git rid of it!" she yells while running out of the bathroom, through our room, into the living room.

Daddy gets a plastic bucket from under the kitchen sink. It only takes him a couple of minutes to catch the rat. When he walks back through our bedroom again, he has a towel over the bucket.

This is just another reason for me to hate our bathroom. Now, when I sit on the toilet, I will keep my legs open to look down into the bowl.

Now that everyone in the house is up, we all get moving. It's going to be nice outside. I wish we could miss school again today and play at the creek, but it will have to wait until we get home. I don't mind, though, since I only have to go to school today and then have two days off.

"Meet me at the sluice, Sarah!" Curtis says as soon as we step off the bus after school. He sounds out of breath as he races up the driveway. He tosses his school stuff at the bottom of the porch steps and takes off.

I will walk up the driveway. *I'm not running after Curtis. I'll just let him win.* I see Daddy working in the garage with both doors open.

As I walk toward the garage, I hear this terrible sound coming from my favorite cat we ever had, Mama Cat. I get a sick feeling in my belly and freeze for a second. It sounds like she's screaming.

Suddenly I stop like I've run into a brick wall. My eyes get big like the moon.

I've got to help her!

Chapter 5
Have to & Watching My Back

I jump off him and run to stand by Curtis,
who's already attacking Johnny again.
I don't like hurting anyone or anything, but I'll fight if I have to,
and protecting Curtis and our special place are a "have to."

Mama is a small black cat with giant green eyes. She gets lots of cuts on her from living in and around the rusted junk cars in our front and back yards. The Junkers lining the driveway belong to Daddy. They're usually missing something: a door, a tire, an engine, a roof, windows, or all the above. Daddy calls our yard a "landmine of metal." "You have to be careful around here not to step on something sharp," he always tells me.

The other vehicles, parked against the creekbank side of the driveway, are waiting for their owners to pick them up once Daddy finishes fixing them.

I started using the car parts for my forts a long time ago because my attempts to make them out of mud never worked. They always fell apart when it rained, and it rains a lot where we live in Carl's Creek.

Mud can also be used for medicine, or so I think. Mother never let me use the stinging spray she sometimes used on my cuts with the sticky bandages to help Mama Cat. She'd always say, "That damn cat don't need it." Daddy laughed when he saw me trying to help her. He'd even give some tape from the garage to hold the mud in place. Mama Cat always tried to run away and pull it off afterward, but I kept putting it on whenever she got hurt.

All I wanna do is help her.

When I find her now, Mama Cat is in front of one of the old cars in the driveway, running in circles like she's trying to bite her tail, making an awful noise. There's a lot of red blood on the fur by the butt.

"Daddy!" I run toward where he's painting a car.

"Dolly, what's wrong?" he shouts over the sound of the compression machine and Elvis's "Hound Dog."

"Something's wrong with Mama Cat! She has blood all over her!"

Daddy turns everything off in the garage. "Dolly, what's going on?"

"She's going in circles and screaming loud and bleeding by her tail," I can barely get the words out.

"The cat is *screaming*?"

"Yes, Daddy, come see her! Come see her! Hurry, Daddy!" I tug his hand and drag him halfway up the driveway.

Mama Cat is still screaming and spinning.

Daddy gets closer, and she leaps away hissing. I see something sticking out of her back end under her tail as she runs off. It looks like little... paws?

My mouth drops open.

"Well, Dolly," Daddy says, "I know what's wrong with her. She's gonna have a litter of kittens."

"Kittens?" I shout, super happy.

"Don't chase her. Cats like to hide to have their kittens." I walk back to the garage with him.

Daddy leaves the door open and makes a bed out of old blankets and newspapers in the back corner of the garage under an old tool chest. I stand by the door and watch him make a special place for Mama Cat. This is definitely not something Mother would do. She is way meaner than Daddy. Why can't she be more like him?

"I'll go in the house and grab Mama Cat a small bowl of milk and put it in the corner. This way maybe she will go to the bed I made for her to have the kittens." "Great idea Daddy. Can I go with you?" "Why don't you stay out here Dolly and try to stop her from running toward the road?"

"Will do," I tell him as he turns and walks up the porch steps and into the house.

It's only minutes before Mama Cat stops spinning in circles and then runs into the garage without any help. I do as Daddy says and stay

outside of the garage to make sure she doesn't run back out and toward the road. Then, suddenly, Mama Cat stops screaming.

"Hey, Dolly, where is Mama Cat?" She ran through the garage door you left open. I don't know where she went inside." Daddy blocks me from walking inside. "Why don't we let her find her own space now?" He steps inside, setting the bowl of milk in the corner where he made the bed. He then stands up, waving his hand toward me to follow him as he walks back to the car on the other side of the garage.

"Dolly, since you're so worried about her, I won't run the compressor, the saw, or play my music until she has her kittens. "She'll want it quiet and warm to have her babies. So, I think it's best if we keep her inside for now."

My pointer finger goes to my lips, making the *shhhh* sound while nodding at Daddy.

I'm so happy Mama Cat has Daddy to help her, just like he helps me.

"Go play, Dolly, and I'll let you know when Mama Cat has the litter," Daddy whispers.

"Okeydokey artichokey," I say quietly and try to wink but can't, so I close both eyes instead of one.

Daddy laughs softly, winks at me, grabs a piece of sanding paper, and begins sanding the front panel of the car he had been working on while I tip-toe out of the garage.

The driveway stones didn't stop me from running as fast as possible. I start counting to see how long it will take me to get to the sluice pipe. I begin counting slowly—one, two, three and finally arrive when I get to seventeen.

I meet Curtis there, and we just start catching minnows when we hear someone shout, "Ouch! I'm getting cut up by these prickers! Turn around!"

Who found our path? We peek through the bushes. There are four kids headed our way. We make tracks fast, running up our path to the trail. Once we reach the road, the kids are already there.

"What are you guys doing here?" Curtis yells.

They all turn around as we continue toward them.

I know who they are. The boy and one of the girls are Johnny and Joanie. They're brother and sister and live down the road. The two other girls are their cousins. I've met them before, but I don't remember their names.

"What are you two doing here?" Johnny raises his eyebrows at us.

"Nothing," I reply. "We were just walking up the path back to our house."

Pointing at her legs, one of the cousins asks, "How can you walk down through the pricker bushes?" My gaze darts to her legs, seeing her bleeding cuts and swollen red scratches.

Johnny then pipes up, "There has to be something cool down there if you walk through all those pricker bushes to get to it."

Crossing my arms, "It's our spot. We know how to get down without getting all cut up. No one else can hang out here."

"Ha," he snorts, "we can go there anytime we want."

"No way," Curtis says. "And if you try, you'll be sorry!"

Whoa, that's my little brother. Curtis looks like he just grew a few inches standing up to them, not like the scaredy-cat he is around our brothers.

"Oh yeah?" they all say at the same time.

"Just watch us," Joanie says, like she thinks she's super-smart.

"We'll fight you for it," Curtis says.

"We don't want to fight," both cousins say at the same time as they back away from us, but Johnny and Joanie don't budge.

I don't want to fight, but I won't give up our favorite spot or share it, so I have no choice.

The cousins yell, "Go!" and Johnny charges toward Curtis, punching him in the mouth.

Curtis's lip splits open again, and blood starts running down his teeth, but that doesn't stop him from diving at Johnny. It's all happening so fast; I just stand there and watch.

And then Joanie comes at me.

My plan to stand here and make her come to me works. She doesn't look that tough with her blonde pigtails, hot pink ruffled shorts, and matching Barbie shirt, so I'm not worried as she lunges toward me.

And when she takes a swing at me, she closes her eyes.

How do you punch someone with your eyes closed?

I don't waste any time. I shove Joanie to the ground and then sit on top of her, pinning her arms to her chest. "Give up!"

She squirms for a few seconds but then squeals like a pig. "I quit! I give up!"

I jump off quickly, keeping my eye on Joanie in case she's dumb enough to come at me once more. I'm glad our fight didn't take very long because now I can focus on what's going on with my brother.

Curtis charges at Johnny again, who shoves him to the ground, making Curtis hit his head on a rock. Johnny jumps on him and keeps punching.

"Ow! Get off me!" Curtis is squiggling like a worm to buck him off. I rip Johnny off Curtis. "No one hurts my little brother. *No one.*"

Then Johnny takes a swing at *me.* He aimed for my face, but he hit my shoulder instead because I moved.

He's off-balance and wobbling, so I act fast. I jump on his back, grabbing his ears.

He spins around, trying to get me off him, making me dizzy. Thankfully, he trips on a rock and falls, giving me a chance to get a better grip.

I don't let go, and when we crash, his arm cracks against another large rock nearby.

"Shit! Get off me!" He tries to take another swing, but from where we landed on the ground, the only thing he's gonna hit is another rock.

I jump and run to stand by Curtis, holding up my fists, ready to attack Johnny again. The cousins are screaming while Joanie stands there with her mouth hanging open, staring at her brother on the ground. I don't like hurting anyone or anything, but I'll fight if I have to, and protecting Curtis and our special place are a "have to."

"Stop!" Joanie yells. "I want to go home."

Johnny looks at all of us. His cousins haven't moved, and his sister is calling it quits. There's no one left to help him, and the two of us aren't going down without a fight.

Johnny gets up, glaring at both Curtis and me.

I step in front of him, blocking his path, and stare right back.

"Move out of my way," he says, sounding gruff.

"If you try to hit my brother again, you'll be sorry." Then I take a few steps back to Curtis's side, giving Johnny a clear path.

He opens his mouth to say something, but the girls interrupt. "Come on, Johnny. Let's go home. Leave them alone."

He brushes off his clothing and spits on my feet. "I guess you *do* need the water in the creek more than we do because you need a bath, Stinky."

I check out my feet for a split second and notice the mud that always seems to be caked on them.

"Let's get out of here. Only scumbags like to play in a creek, anyway," one of the cousins says while looking right at me.

"Never come back here. *Ever!*" I yell as loud as I can.

Johnny walks off, taking the lead up the road. "C'mon, girls. Let's leave these losers alone."

They high-tail it up the road after him.

It felt so good for Curtis and me to fight together for what we wanted.

When we can't see them anymore, I explode with happiness. "We did it, Curtis! We did it!" I give him a high-five while jumping up and down.

Curtis doesn't return it.

"What's wrong?"

"Sarah, I didn't need your help." Then he scowls at me and stomps off toward home. I don't know what to say as I watch him walk away.

The walnut tree across from our fort has a little stump under it that makes a perfect chair. So rather than following Curtis, I sit.

Curtis is mad at me?

Bending forward, I put my head in my hands, resting on my knees, and cry. "What did I do wrong?" Was I supposed to let Johnny beat the crap out of him? No way I was going to let that happen. I've never seen Curtis act so tough. How was I supposed to know that he would become this big bad fighter? And, why now? Of all days, he picks this one to actually talk and fight. Why can't he help me fight Mother for more food or toast? Why?

As I raise my head to look down the road, he is gone. I can't go home yet.

I need to be alone.

After a couple cars go by, I knew I'd been sitting here for quite a while because we don't live on a busy road. Walking home seems to take forever. I wasn't happy and skipping like I usually do or racing my brother. It was just me.

I poke my head into the garage, "Daddy," I say loud enough that he can hear, but not too loud for Mama Cat.

As I wait for his answer, I hear soft meows coming from the back

35

of the garage. Then, finally, Daddy appears from the side of the shiny black Mustang he had been sanding when I left.

"Mama Cat had six kittens. We need to keep quiet a while longer, but I got work to do first thing in the morning, so we have to move them to a new place tonight after supper. Before we move them, they'll need a new bed."

"I'm on it, Daddy!" I say, smiling big. I'm starting to feel better as I back out of the door, closing it gently behind me.

I get to work right away, picking out the old blue car with its rusted, spotted doors for Mama Cat and the kitties' new home. The windows are gone, and the handle is broken in half. It'd had four doors once, but the one where the driver sits is off and leaning against the car. It has gray blocks underneath it instead of tires.

Our neighbor, Mr. Bob, lives across the road and has a goat pen in his backyard. Curtis and I named the goats Larry and Bertha. I'll get hay from the pen for the bed.

I cross my fingers and hope I won't get caught lifting the latch on the goats' pen.

Larry starts chewing on my shorts and almost knocks me over as I collect a big scoop of hay right where he's standing and fold up my shirt to carry all of it.

The gate latch isn't very strong, and those goats know how to open it so they can "explore the neighborhood," as Daddy likes to say. Still, I somehow get it to shut and lock it without Larry or Bertha escaping. And I don't even drop any of the hay out of my shirt. *Yahoo!*

After making my way back across the road without getting caught, I create a nice cozy bed for the new family.

Daddy hollers, "Dolly, time for dinner."

Curtis ignores me all through supper. *He can't stay mad at me forever.*

Then, finally, Daddy and I head back outside to move the kittens to their new home when we finish eating. "I have just the spot for them," I say while skipping to the garage. Carrying two of them is hard because they are wriggling in my hands, and I almost drop them but somehow manage to get them to their new home. After that, Daddy carried the remaining four.

I get down on the ground and place all the kittens behind the propped-up door. When I put the last kitty on the hay, Mama Cat comes and plops down with them, letting her babies crawl all over her.

"We did it, Daddy!"

"We sure did, honey."

As soon as we get back inside, I hear Mother tell Daddy that she wants to go with him when he plays at the Bear Claw tonight. I can't believe they're going out two nights in a row. I wish I could go listen to Daddy sing. They're leaving after she puts Emma, Curtis, and me to bed.

Oh no! Please let my older brothers leave us alone while they're gone!

After they leave, I lie awake, listening for the boys to come into our room, but I'm too tired to keep my eyes open, and before I know it, I must have fallen asleep.

Curtis is picked on the most by our brothers. They're mean to both of us, but they like to trick him more with pranks.

Most nights, Curtis is a heavy sleeper, and I hear him snoring loudly. He breathes through his mouth 'cause Daddy says he has "adenoid trouble." When I look at him puzzled, he says, "Nose trouble, Dolly."

My brother's laughing wakes me up, and that's when I see they are doing something to Curtis. I'm so scared it's like I'm tied to the bed and can't move.

I peek at them to see what's so funny, but I'm careful not to let them know I'm awake.

Vinnie dips both ends of a Q-tip into a jar of peanut butter and then hands it to Terry.

"Jam it up his damn nose," Derek whispers to him.

I'm so scared Curtis will stop breathing and die if they do that. They know he has nose trouble because Daddy told me right in front of them.

Vinnie and Derek are standing next to Terry, watching him do it and trying not to wake Curtis up. I'm scared of them, but I still would stand up for Curtis if Derek wasn't here. Plus, Curtis is already mad at me for sticking up for him at the fight today, so I might make him madder.

I'm lying on my bed, waiting for Curtis to stop breathing. I feel like *I* can't breathe as I think about it.

My brother is going to die.

Terry leans toward Curtis, and, suddenly, Curtis sits up, coughing and gagging. At the same time, the boys are bent over, holding their stomachs. "Did you see that chunk of booger butter come flying out his nose?" Vinnie said while laughing at Curtis. "Stop, I'm going to throw up!" Terry yells.

Vinnie and Terry are looking and pointing at Curtis while they laugh, but Derek is staring at *me*.

I squeeze my eyes shut tight, hoping he didn't see me looking at him just now. I try so hard to keep from shaking, wondering if they're going to put peanut butter up my nose or do something worse. Thankfully, though, this is all they do, then they leave us alone— but I can't fall back to sleep.

I wish I could run away from Derek and the others, but I would be scared to be outside all alone by myself. I wonder if Mama Cat feels that same way? Why did they have to use peanut butter in Curtis's nose? That's my favorite thing to put on a sandwich. Why can't they just leave Curtis and me alone? *Why?*

Once the boys leave, I open my eyes to make sure they're gone, only to see Derek stick his head back in our room through the door. He mouths to me, pointing, "You're next." Sadly, I know Derek means what he says.

"Sarah?"

I'm already on my way down to Curtis. I climb into bed with my brother hugging him while he cries. "My nose hurts, Sarah." "I'm sure it does. Can you breathe, okay?" He takes a couple deep breaths while picking peanut butter out of his nose with his finger.

"I'm sorry Curtis." I remember Derek's threat.

I'm going to have to watch my back even more than before.

Chapter 6
Stop & The Coolest Daddy Ever

"Curtis, no! Stop!" I shout in a voice that sounds much younger
and higher than my own.
I see him jump, startled.
Then, quickly, he yanks his hands up from the water,
and I see something bobbing up to the top of it.

One more day off before I have to go back to school. I look out the window by my bed, and the sun is shining through all the gray clouds for the second day in a row, which doesn't often happen around here.

I move fast this morning to get outside and check on the kittens. I ate breakfast fast, but not as fast as Curtis. Taking two steps at a time, I reach the bottom of the porch. My head turns in every direction making sure Curtis isn't in sight.

Hurrying up the driveway, I drop down on my knees in front of the car door where we left all of them last night. There they are, Mama with her kittens, sleeping on the hay I had taken for them to use as a bed. One, two, three, four, five…

I stop… and count again. My heart thumps in my chest. Where's the sixth kitten?

I walk around the car to see if I can find it, but it's nowhere.

A terrible thought hits me, and I feel hot and cold all at the same time.

Curtis found the kittens.

And I know exactly where he's gone— to our sluice pipe fort. It's not the first time Curtis has taken an animal there.

I rush to the creek, breathing hard, but still trying to be careful as I zip past the old cars, which can catch my clothes or skin on the sharp parts sticking out. The farther I go, the harder my heart beats until it pounds inside me like a big, metal drum.

As fast as I can, I run out the driveway, down the road. Once I'm on the pricker path, my toe catches on a sharp rock, and blood runs across my dirty feet. It hurts like someone stabbed me with a needle. I don't slow down, though. As I get close to it, there is no sign of my little brother. Finally, I reach the point where the creek meets our sluice pipe and climb into the tunnel.

There he is, kneeling at the other end, close to the water's edge. His head is down, and I notice his hands are in the water.

"Curtis, no! Stop!" I shout in a voice that sounds much younger and higher than my own.

I see him jump, startled. Then, quickly, he yanks his hands up, and I see something bobbing up to the top of the water.

The missing kitten is there, in front of Curtis, floating.

I push past Curtis, and he slides away. I drop to my knees and scoop up the kitten. I lift it, staring at its lifeless body. It has the same color coat as its mother. I don't know its eye color because they're still closed. I think that they might never open now.

The fur hangs from its body like our weeping willow tree branches. Softly, I stroke the kitty's face with my finger, hoping it'll move. *Move! Breathe!*

Nothing happens.

Now my face is as wet as the kittens. I'm crying tears so big they seem to be coming from a grown-up's eyes.

I don't know how long I kneel there, sobbing. Time seems to have stopped. I can hardly see from all the tears. Blind, just like the kitten.

I look back at Curtis, but he's already out of the tunnel and in the creek chasing minnows. It's as if he's forgotten that he just killed a kitten. I want to scream and ask why he'd do something like this, but I can't think about anything other than the dead kitten.

My chest feels like a giant fist is squeezing it. I make a noise that sounds like the yelp Maisy makes when someone accidentally steps on her tail.

No. I shake my head hard, though no one is there to see me do it.

I'm not letting this kitten die.

Rubbing its back seems like the best thing to do. I coo softly and whisper the way my family did with Emma when she was a baby. "Please come back to me, little kitty." I turn it around and around in my hands, hoping this will make it breathe again.

Before I look at Curtis, I stare at the baby animal, looking for any sign of life. I don't know why I keep looking at him. Maybe I'm hoping he'll run back and try to help, but all I see is his back; he keeps playing in the water like nothing terrible has happened.

It looks like this pretty little black kitten will need a funeral.

"Sarah, help!" Curtis splashes around in the water, yanking at his foot that appears stuck in the mud. No matter how hard he tugs to get it out, nothing's working.

Before helping Curtis, I take the kitten over to the bank to set it down in the tall grass by the side of the creek.

Just before I do— The kitten moves its head!

"The kitty is alive, Curtis!"

He either doesn't hear me or doesn't care. He's still fighting with the water, mud, and his shoe. "Hey, Sarah, are you gonna help me or what?"

Holding the kitten close to my chest with one hand, I pull Curtis free of the mud with the other.

He fishes around in the water for his shoe. Then, finally, he pulls it out and drags himself onto the bank. I'm already there, still cradling the kitty.

"Curtis, why did you do that to the kitten?" I ask while the little black drenched baby lies in my lap. He shrugs and says nothing. My voice gets louder. "Why did you try to drown this kitten? It did nothing to you?"

"I don't know!" he shouts back as he puts his head down and turns away from me, walking back into the creek.

Now, all I can do is stare at my little brother, wanting him to tell me how he can be so mean. I don't want him acting like Derek, Vinnie, and Terry, because this is something they would do. I knew Curtis didn't like animals, but I don't know why. Still sitting on the side of the bank, stroking the wet fur of the kitty, I watch him catch minnows as I try to understand what just happened at our sluice fort.

I spend a long time cuddling the kitten and whispering to it, thinking about what I will name the tiny but strong little one. *This kitty is like me.* Even when bad things happen to it, it doesn't give up. At least today, it didn't. So today is its lucky day.

41

"That's it!" I say out loud to no one since Curtis won't care even if he hears me. I look down at the baby, now coming back to life and rolling around in my hands. "I don't know if you are a boy or girl kitty, but I'm going to pretend you're a girl but tough like a boy—just like me. I'm going to name you Lucky," I tell her. She makes a soft, meowing sound, and I take that to mean she likes it.

Curtis waded around in the creek, stabbing at the minnows with a stick and kicking water into the air. Then, he jumps out and onto the bank with a splash. "Let's go," he says like nothing has happened.

But it has. And I won't ever forget.

I tuck Lucky inside my shirt as we silently walk back home. My heart feels like it's exploding with love for the squirming furball against my chest. This is the first time I've saved a kitten from Curtis. This kitty is mine now, and I love her. I'll do whatever I have to do to keep her safe. "Sarah and Curtis, get your damn asses in the house for lunch," I hear Mother yelling at us as soon as we hit the driveway. From her tone, I know we need to get in the house quickly to avoid getting in trouble. Curtis runs straight home. I race through the front yard to find the blue car with the spots on the door and return Lucky to her Mama and brothers and sisters. Mama Cat watches as if she knows I rescued her baby and is trying to thank me. She purrs and meows as I lay Lucky near her, who is quick to get some milk.

"Sarah!"

I bolt for the house as Mother yells to me at the top of her lungs.

I'll come back for you, I tell Lucky in my mind. *I'll keep you safe. I promise.*

I finish lunch, but know I need to wait until Curtis heads back to the sluice pipe before moving the kitties and Mama Cat again.

There's a gigantic tree near the end of the driveway with another broken-down car next to it. This is a good hiding spot, but I hate moving the kittens this close to the road because they could wander off and get killed. However, their chances are better here than anywhere Curtis might be able to find them. Also, since Daddy doesn't allow us to play this close to the road, Curtis won't think to cross the driveway to look here. I may not always listen to Mother, but Curtis knows I do what Daddy tells me, so he won't find this hiding spot.

I put the kittens under the car door, propped up against the green, rusty car, then go back for the others. Mama Cat meows and follows me to their new home when I pick up the last two kitties.

"Hello," I say to Lucky, who looks at me like she already knows my voice. My heart feels like it is so big and so warm that it might pop out of my chest at any minute now.

Mama Cat darts off toward the weeds. They're meowing really loud. I can understand 'cause it'd be really sad not knowing where you are or why your Mama or Daddy isn't around— even though the daddy cats are not always nice to their babies. It's just the opposite of my house.

I whisper, "Your mama will be back soon." At least the brothers and sisters are together. Knowing Curtis and I are together keeps me going when Daddy isn't in the house.

When I think I've pushed my luck long enough, I hurry back to the sluice pipe before Daddy catches me or—worse— before Curtis wanders around and finds me with the kitties. I spend the rest of the day with Curtis, trying to keep an eye on him.

As soon as we walk in the front door, Mother yells, "Curtis, git in the tub and take your bath." I'm still mad at him and can't understand why he'd want to hurt something so tiny. He knows what it feels like to be hurt by someone bigger than you.

Telling myself that he is young and doesn't know better isn't helping. Daddy said one time, "Curtis's a good kid; he just has a lot of growing up to do and a lot of feelings he needs to sort out for himself." So, when Mother would complain to Daddy about Curtis, he would tell her that Curtis is young for his age.

Curtis must not understand what he was doing or know it was wrong.

He's hurt animals before. I don't know why, and I don't know how to make him stop.

He would kick Maisy whenever our brothers were mean to him. I'm sure that Curtis never hurt Maisy when Daddy was around.

But I've learned to watch out for animals whenever our brothers hurt him, and I've gotten pretty good at it.

At least, that's what I've thought until today.

I hear the water running in the bathroom. Curtis's bath. I wonder how he would feel if Mother came in while he was washing up and held his head underwater. I don't want him dead, and I don't want Mother to ever do this sort of thing to him. But how would he like it?

43

"Make sure you're washin' your damn hair," Mother yells at Curtis. He never washes it the way she wants. She has her way of doing things, and that's how we're supposed to do everything. There's no arguing with her unless you're older like Derek, Vinnie, and Terry.

Maybe when I get to be their age, I'll yell at Mother too, and tell her to stop putting my hands under the hot water. I'll demand more toast, and I won't take *no* for an answer.

I wait on my bunk bed, keeping the dried mud from falling onto my mattress.

There's a noise coming from outside. The sound of the sander is calling my name. Next to painting, sanding is my favorite job to do with Daddy. So, I lower myself from the bunk and dash out to the garage to see if I can help him.

"Hey, Bucky, where you going in such a hurry?" Terry's on the couch watching television.

I hate it when he calls me names! I keep my head down and go out the door without saying a word to him.

Many of the kids in my class gave me the same nickname. A girl at my school had once asked me, "Why do your teeth stick out so far? They even hang over your bottom lip. You look like a buck-tooth beaver." Everybody laughed, and the kids who'd heard her started calling me Bucky.

I try not to let it bother me and tell myself that they are just dumb, D-U-M.

At the bottom of the porch steps, there is a hole on the path to the garage. Our sidewalk is gray with lots of cracks in it. Sometimes little yellow flowers grow up in the middle of a crack until Curtis picks them. If anyone forgets about the hole when they step off the porch, they'll definitely twist their ankle. It's happened to me many times. I should remember it's there, but I don't always pay attention to it when I'm in a hurry to see Daddy.

While bending down just inside the garage door, I hear Daddy. "Good girl, putting those boots on before coming in. We want to protect those little feet of yours."

Mother wouldn't even care about protecting my feet.

When I do forget, Daddy doesn't have to say a word—Just sings, "To work, wear boots. To paint, wear boots. To run the sander, wear boots. To be like Daddy, wear boots. To play, *leave* the boots." He made up this little song to help me remember when I had to wear them. When I forget, and I do a lot, he never gets mad at me.

Daddy's playing music on his 8-track tape and singing along to it. "Country roads, take me home…" His voice is deep when he sings.

I run to the shelf Daddy built just for me beside his workbench. I keep my supplies there, like my safety glasses and the purple toolbox he bought for me.

Daddy is under one of the cars, still singing. I join in. He pushes his little wheeled cart out, "Sing it, Dolly!"

I hadn't loved the nickname at first because it sounded so girly. But once Daddy explained why he'd given it to me, I started loving it—almost as much as I love him. Daddy never calls me Bucky. He doesn't hold my hands under scorching hot water, and he doesn't say or do all the horrible things to me like everyone else except for Emma and Curtis.

But, unlike most people in my family, he always seems glad to see me.

Daddy sits up on his cart and opens his arms.

I jump in them.

He chuckles and gives me a giant squeeze. "I'm so happy to see you. Are you up to helping me today?"

"Yup, I sure am, Daddy!" But I don't want to let go of his neck 'cause he always smells good, even after working in the garage all day. "Why do you smell so good?" I ask. "Old Spice," he says. So, the next time I'm in the bathroom, I'm going to look for it to spray it on my pillow.

I roll my own cart over to Daddy. I lie back on it, and he does the same with his. We slide under the car together at the same time.

Daddy points at the muffler.

"Why is there a hole in it?" I ask.

"A rock on the road could cause a hole, Dolly, or maybe they hit a big pothole."

"What are you going to do to fix it?"

"I think the torch is the best option we have here, Miss Dolly," he says with a wink.

It's a rule that I must step away from the car when Daddy is using the torch. So, when he's doing something dangerous in one garage stall, I must be in the other one.

As told, I roll out from under the car and go to my stool to watch him work. It's always so much fun to be in the garage with him. I would stay there all the time if Mother let me.

Before she sends us outside to play, she tells me the same thing every... single... time. "And Sarah, don't ya go botherin' your father while he's busy workin', ya hear?"

If Mother forgets to say it, game-on for me to spend as long as I want in my favorite place in the world: in the garage with Daddy.

Mother must know nothing about what Daddy does in the garage because he calls me his garage mascot when I go in there to see him. He never tells me to leave, and he never tells me I'm bothering his work. When Daddy gets a car for painting, he has to tape it before starting. He runs large rolls of tape along the side, and while he's working, he asks, "Dolly, does that tape look even to you?"

My answer is always the same: "It sure does, Daddy." It's an honest answer because he always makes the tape perfectly straight. I've never seen him tape off a car any other way.

When he finishes his work, we clean up the garage together, and then Daddy plays the guitar. He sits on his bench stool while I sit on the cement floor by his feet and asks, "What would you like to hear me play?"

"Play Dolly Parton!" I tell him.

"How about 'A Coat of Many Colors'?"

That's my favorite Dolly Parton song. She sings about other kids making fun of her coat, but she likes it anyway. I lean my head against Daddy's leg, close my eyes, and listen to him play and sing. I have the coolest Daddy ever. I will stay here forever, working on cars and listening to him play.

When the song is over, I hear Mother's angry shout, "Is Sarah out there?" She's not happy that I'm not in the house to take a bath after Curtis. She's trying not to sound too mean as she always does when Daddy is around, but I can tell Mother is upset—like she always gets when I'm out in the garage. "The garage is no place for a girl," she says. But I'm not like other girls. And Daddy teaches me so many things, which he says are good for me to know.

"Yes, Donna. I'll bring her in once we clean everything up." But we've already cleaned up.

I hold my breath, waiting for Mother to shout again. When she doesn't, I blow out the big breath I held and smile to myself. He's sticking up for me.

As soon as we walk in the door, our dog Maisy slowly manages to get up off her rug and walks over to us, wagging her tail. "Hi girl," I say, petting her black fur with as much gray and white as it does black. "Hello Maisy, what a good girl you are," Daddy scratches her ears as he talks, not in his usual voice.

Then, after only a few minutes, Maisy limps back over to her bed and flops down. Poor Maisy. I like to pet her when I'm in the house, which isn't often if I can help it. When Mother lets her outside during the day to go potty, and I'm around playing in the mud—I will stop what I'm doing and pet her.

But, as soon as Mother sees us together, she calls her back in the house.

When Daddy spends any time inside, Maisy follows him around in the house and likes to sit by his chair. She is not the only one who sticks to him like glue.

Daddy always tells me that I'd run into him if he ever stops walking, "Dolly, are you my shadow?" he'll ask me.

I'm not sure what he means, but I will be if being close to him makes me his shadow. The only place he doesn't allow me to follow him is into the bathroom unless he's fixing something or shaving, and then he'll let me sit on the sink so I can watch him do both.

Tonight, Daddy sits in his recliner in the living room. He picks up a car magazine and starts reading. I immediately sit on the floor next to him.

I don't want to lie to Daddy, so I take a big breath and let it out. "Daddy, I have to tell you something." He puts down his magazine and turns his head to the floor, looking at me. "I put Mama Cat and her kitties under a car on the other side of the driveway, by the weeping willow tree." All the words come out so fast that I don't stop to breathe.

Daddy frowns just a little. "Why would you move them that close to the road? We talked about you not going past that tree."

"Curtis doesn't like the kittens, so I moved them where he couldn't find them."

Daddy raises his eyebrows, "I'm sure you must have your reasons."

47

I trust you, Dolly. We've talked about how to be safe on the road. When you are playing by it, that's a different story. Make sure you do not sit on the berm of the road. I want your back to the driveway and you facing the road so you can see what is coming. Deal?" He holds his hand up for a high-five slap. *Smack!*

"Deal."

He doesn't ask more questions and doesn't yell at me like Mother would do. Instead, he smiles at me and says, "Honey, someday you will save the world."

I smile back, showing him my teeth. Daddy never makes fun of my big teeth like my older brothers and the kids at school, so I always give him my biggest smiles.

I can help save the world... But why does the world need to be saved? And what am I supposed to do to save it? I've been kind to Maisy when Curtis was mean to her. I've hidden many cats and kittens from Curtis. I've moved a bird's nest with eggs, rescued a toad and a baby bunny, and made a pet out of a spider. And then there is Lucky, my best save ever.

But who's going to save me from Mother and Derek?

Chapter 7
I'll Get You My Pretty & Making Mud Pies.

That night, when I go to sleep, I see the Wicked Witch in my nightmare.
She has Mother's face and says,
"I'll get you, my pretty, and your kitty cats, too!"
I wake up, shivering from both the dream and the cold.

One hot summer day, Curtis and I were at the sluice pipe when we smelled something awful. When I climbed up the creek bank to the road, I saw a smushed animal with flies all over it. I threw up in my mouth because it was so disgusting and guts smashed everywhere.

I've never forgotten that horrible sight and smell, and that's exactly how the house smells tonight. I don't ask Mother what she's making or complain about it. Even with Daddy in the house, though he won't get angry, he doesn't like any of us talking bad about Mother's cooking. "I work hard to make money to buy this food, and your mother works hard to prepare it, so we should just eat it."

As Daddy heads to the back of the house, Terry walks in, makes a face, and says to Mother, "Gosh, what the hell is that smell? It's stinking up the whole damn house."

Mother doesn't get mad at Terry, and Daddy doesn't hear him, so he gets away with the mean comment.

"We're havin' cabbage 'n ham for supper tonight," Mother shouts.

Terry shakes his head, then plops onto the sofa in front of the picture window, picking up Daddy's car book. He doesn't read it but flips through looking at the pictures.

When Daddy tells me it's my turn for my bath, I pass Curtis on his bed. He's playing with some little plastic green figures that used to belong to our older brothers. I get a quick bath, put on my pajamas, and, just as I finish, Mother yells. "Get your asses out here. It's time for supper."

49

Derek is sitting at the table. Yucky food with my yucky brother. At least Daddy is here for supper tonight.

We all take our seats. Water runs from the green stuff under the pink meat.

Vinnie sighs and whispers, "I hate ham and cabbage." Then, quickly looks up and sees Daddy giving him the stink eye. He swallows hard, lowers his head, and eats without another word about it.

I will be eating very little for supper tonight. Mother always yells, "You're too damn picky about food for your own good." I am a fussy eater, and Mother says I need to learn to eat all foods, not just toast, peanut butter and jelly sandwiches, and cereal. She is right about one thing: those are the only foods I like.

Maisy cuddles against my feet under the table during dinner. I learned the trick of dropping my food to her after I got sick from eating peas. First, I pretend to eat. Then, when Mother turns to feed Emma, I take whatever food I don't like and drop it on the floor for Maisy.

One bite of Mother's ham and cabbage is the last bite I'll take if I can help it. Emma drops her spoon, which is the perfect time for my food dropping plan.

Daddy's the only one who seems to look around the table during supper, but I don't think he saw what I did. And then our eyes meet, and he winks. *What in the world?* Daddy knows what I did and isn't mad at me for doing it. I wonder, *is he taking my side over Mother?*

I can't believe he isn't telling her what I did.

"Sarah, stop playin' with your food and eat it," Mother hollers at me.

We're eating dinner at 6:30 tonight. We usually eat at 6:00, and then Curtis and I go to bed at 8:30. Mother even had me get a bath before supper, which is not our regular routine. The boys are trying to finish their meal in a hurry to get away from the table to leave and hang out with their friends, but Mother has other plans for them. "I want everyone in front of the television at 8:00 tonight, to watch a show together."

The boys say together, "Oh mom," but Daddy clears his throat like he's about to cough.

He always makes that noise when he wants the boys to listen, but he doesn't do that with me.

It works. Vinnie and Terry stop arguing and go quiet.

Daddy winks.

He said a wink means he loves me.

Mother spoons some orange food from a tiny jar into Emma's mouth, "Do ya have plans tomorrow night?" she looks over at Derek.

"Nope. I did, but they got canceled," he says with a full mouth of chewed-up food.

Oh yuck, it looks like Maisy's canned dog food, only a different color.

I'm just about to drop some more of this gross supper down to Maisy when Mother asks, "Derek, can ya stick around the house tomorrow night and watch the kids? Your Father and I are goin' out for our anniversary." I freeze as I wait for Derek's answer. Will it be The Book Game, The Boxing Game, or something new if he watches us?

They've made us play Run from the BBs, where they shoot at us with a BB gun—and when the BBs hit us, they really hurt.

But the worst is the doctor game Derek only plays with me. I've gone to the Doctor, and he didn't do to me what Derek does. He takes me into his bedroom, looks down at my shirt, then says, "Nope, not yet," whatever that means.

Mother never notices how upset Curtis and I get when she asks Derek, Vinnie, and Terry to watch us. I'm sure she'd never believe me if I told her about Derek playing Doctor. She'd just say I'm a liar and hold my hands under hot water for a long time. I want to talk to Daddy about it, but I'm worried Derek might come up with an even meaner game if I do or, worse, hurt Curtis, which he always threatens to do if I don't do what he wants.

I put my head down on the table after hearing Mother ask Derek to watch us.

I can feel Daddy's eyes on me.

"What's wrong, Dolly? You need to eat your dinner. You're getting too thin."

If only I could tell him what the boys do when we're alone with them. If Daddy knew they hurt us, they'd get in a lot of trouble.

But I'm afraid of what they'll do to us if I tell.

My plate is still full of cabbage when everyone else finishes eating.

Mother sets the timer on the stove, which she often does when I eat too slowly for her liking. "Young lady, if ya don't have that food gone by the time this goes off, ya'll eat it for breakfast."

My eyes water, and my throat burns. The timer is ticking.

I eat. Thankfully, I manage to get it all down before the bell rings. On other occasions, when Mother sets it this way, I hear Daddy in another room talking to her very quietly, "Donna, let her get up from the table. It's okay if she doesn't like something." She always tells him, no, and Daddy never argues about it.

Mother puts Emma to bed and cleans up the kitchen. Daddy goes back out to the garage for a little while when the boys take their showers.

Our living room is not big enough for us to sit together, so Curtis and I often sit or lie on the floor. My favorite place is by the heating vent closest to Daddy's chair.

Before our older brothers come into the room, Curtis decides to sit on the couch, lifting the cushions first to look under them. He always does this, but I'm the only one willing to get up so he can.

"What the hell are you doing flipping all the damn cushions before you sit down, Curtis?" Derek says, walking into the living room. His voice echoes as he shouts at him. "He's looking for snakes. You're always scaring him about snakes coming to get him. Now he won't sit down without checking under everything," Vinnie reminds Derek as he too stands there watching him.

One by one, the brothers make Curtis move so they can sit on the couch until he ends up on the floor like me. I don't know why he doesn't sit on the floor in the first place; he knows that's where he'll end up once everyone comes into the room.

Just exactly like Mother wanted, we're all sitting in the living room in front of the television by 8:00. We hardly ever do this kind of thing, so I'm wondering what we're going to watch, but asking Mother would be like getting cut by the pricker bushes *on purpose*.

Mother turns on the television, and I see the words, *The Wizard of Oz*. My older brothers roll their eyes and make unhappy noises when the show starts. Curtis and I cannot take our eyes off the colorful, magical movie. It'd be better if there were no commercials. Daddy's looking at me watch this show, but I'm way too interested in the movie to turn away. The Wicked Witch of the West scares me, but I love Dorothy and her little dog, Toto, and Glinda the Good Witch.

Mother sits looking at a book, so I don't know why we all have to be in the living room together. "We have family time tonight, so shut up and be quiet," she yells at the boys just when the movie starts. Family time? What does that mean? I've never heard her say something like that before. The boys talk and goof around all through the movie. "This is stupid shit. Why do we have to watch this baby movie?" Vinnie yells at Mother. Daddy clears his throat and opens his mouth just as Mother slams down her book. She wrinkles up her face and begins yelling at him. "Because you do, so shut up and watch it." Daddy's mouth closes, and he nods.

In the movie, the good witch is trying to help Dorothy when Vinnie says, "I'd like to take Glinda for a ride on my bed." "That's enough of that," Daddy joins in on the conversation. I don't know what Vinnie is talking about because his bed doesn't have wheels. So, how could he take Glinda for a ride on his bed? Even with all the noise and arguing from my brothers, it doesn't stop Curtis and me from watching the movie.

That night, when I go to sleep, I see the Wicked Witch in my nightmare. She has Mother's face and says to me, "I'll get you, my pretty, and your kitty cats, too!" I wake up, shivering from both the dream and the cold. Curtis has taken my sheet and blanket in the middle of the night. I'm curled into a little ball around my pillow, trying to keep warm.

The following day, Curtis says nothing, but since he's completely covered with my sheet and blanket and his too, I'm guessing he was as scared as me last night.

Before my feet touch the floor, Mother is doing her usual morning routine. "Come on, you two, git up and eat so ya can git outside."

Sunday morning. We have the same routine on Saturdays and Sundays as long as the weather isn't too bad: eat breakfast, go outside until lunch. Then after, we go back out until she calls us for dinner. Some nights we get a bath; others, we go to bed with whatever dirt we got on us that day. I don't usually mind getting cleaned up, but my pillow smells worse whenever I smell better.

"Curtis I'm going to the garage today to help Daddy. Do you want to come with me?"

"Nah, I'm going to Timmy's," he says. Daddy always tries to get Curtis to work with us, but he never does.

Quietly, I try to sneak through the living room without Mother seeing me. That don't work. "Sarah, don't go botherin' your father none today. He's got too much work to do."

Ugh! I stomp outside as Curtis hops on his bike and heads to Timmy's house. Oh well, I wanted to check on Mama Cat and her babies without him around anyway. Underneath the green car, the kittens are meowing and purring this morning. Mama Cat is lying on the hay while her kittens eat and play. "Good morning, kitties. I'm happy to see you' re okay."

Lucky picks up her head as if she understands.

After hanging out with the kitties, it's mud pie making time because the sun is shining.

After collecting the water and dirt in my bucket, it's time to begin.

As I work on my masterpieces, a noise, sounding like a car, is coming up the road and catches my attention. Vehicles aren't on our road often, unless they're Daddy's customers, and he usually doesn't have anyone drop them off on the weekend. Plus, it sounds different. Louder. Bigger.

Who or what is coming to our house?

Chapter 8
Looking Stupid & The Blue Bus

*Mrs. Scott asked all the kids to find their names on the
desk and sit down. I didn't know how to read,
so I kept walking around.
"Who's that weird girl with the big teeth and dirty clothes walking
around the desks and looking stupid?
Don't get too close to her, or you might get cooties!"
Mrs. Scott saw me standing in the back of the classroom.
"Please find your seat with your name on the tag hanging off your
desk." I pick one of two empty desks.
"Angela." She looked right at me. "Angela, you need to tell me you're
here when I call your name.
Kids were laughing.
"My name is Sarah."
The teacher pointed to the letters on the empty desk. I didn't know a
single one. "Class, Sarah was testing me this morning to see if I was
paying attention. Give me two days to get to know
your faces with your names, and then we'll play a name game like
Sarah did this morning with me. Thank you, Sarah, for keeping me on
my toes." I just looked at her, my eyes big and my mouth open.
I hadn't tricked Mrs. Scott. I wasn't sure why she'd stuck up for me, but
I liked it.*

Whatever is coming this way has a big motor and sounds like a huge
vehicle. I follow the direction of the sound, and a blue bus is driving
slowly past. This is not the first time it's gone by my house.

*Why is this bus blue instead of yellow, and why is it here on the
weekend?*

55

The people and the kids on the bus are looking out the window at me. The driver gets my attention, and for some reason, I smile and wave.

I watch it go up the road and know that it must come back down because it is a dead-end street.

The engine becomes louder the closer it gets. I drop the dirt and head up the driveway to get a better look. The bus rumbles down the street. There is writing on its side, but I can't make out what it says.

Reading is hard for me. When we read in class, I mix up my words. The kids laugh when I do it. My first-grade teacher, Mrs. Scott, was nice and never yelled as Mother does. She was my first teacher since I didn't go to kindergarten like the other kids because Mother said she, "forgot to send me."

The bus driver pulls over in front of my house, turns off the engine, and opens his window.

"Hi there! My name is Dave. What's your name?"

"Sarah."

His face looks happy as he says, "Sarah, huh? Well, that's just a beautiful name. It's a name in the Bible, you know?"

I don't know what a Bible is, but Dave seems pretty happy about my name being in it. "Sarah, would you like to come to church? We'll take you there. Hop on the bus!"

There are kids on the bus who are laughing, and if they're that happy about going to church, it must be a fun place.

"Is there a Bible at church?"

Dave tilts his head to the side, then nods. "Why, of course, there is."

I feel a little silly for asking, but Dave doesn't look mean or like he thought my question was funny. *Alrighty then.* I walk toward the bus, wiping my hands on my shorts. I know Mother hates it when I don't move fast enough, so I hurry so the bus won't leave without me.

Standing at the top of the stairs, I freeze.

Everyone stops what they are doing and looks at me. That's when an old lady in the front seat wearing a pretty blue dress says, "Sarah, you can sit here with me. But, first, do you need to ask your mother if you're allowed to come with us?"

Mother locks us out of the house during the day and doesn't look for us 'til lunch. Since it's early morning, I have plenty of time before she will look for me, so I tell the old lady, "No." She pats the seat next to her, and

I sit down quickly. The kids immediately go back to talking and laughing. The lady sticks out her hand and tells me her name is Sandy. Like Daddy taught me, I shake it and look right at her. It's hard to see her eyes because she is wearing glasses with black frames. Her hair is dark underneath with gray all over, pinned up with two sticks going through it. Her lips are bright pink, and her teeth are as straight as the lines Daddy makes when he tapes off a car. They're also very white. I don't like my teeth and try to hide them by closing my lips. But it never works because my front teeth stick out over my lip anyway—at least the one that isn't broken.

Dave revs the engine. Once he closes the door, he puts the bus in gear, and we're off. I know all about what Dave is doing because I may not read very well, but I know a lot about the things Daddy works on in the garage.

Miss Sandy and I both turn our heads toward the window at the same time. My mud pies are baking in the sun, where I left them.

Mother won't care if I go to church as long as I'm back for lunch, but Daddy might. I'm not supposed to go anywhere with strangers, but I'm on a bus with Dave and Miss Sandy, and they know my name, so it's okay to go with them, right?

I turn to face the window next to our seat again. Daddy is standing in the driveway watching us pull away, looking up and down the bus. He blows me a kiss when he finds me, then waves goodbye. Both Miss Sandy and I wave back at Daddy.

He turns and heads back into the garage, and then my house grows smaller and smaller until it's out of sight. When I can't see it at all anymore, I turn to face the front window again as the bus travels over the bridge above our sluice pipe.

Where is this bus taking me? It's going in a direction I've never gone before.

I hope it's someplace good.

The houses and stores fly past as we pick up speed. We don't seem to go very far on the bus ride to school, just past the park and one stop sign. But we are going past places I've never seen before.

Maybe I should've asked Miss Sandy or Dave when we would be home before I got on this bus. So, I turn to ask her, and she's talking to a girl sitting behind us. Daddy taught me it isn't nice to interrupt people when they're talking to others, so I stay quiet.

"Will they ever stop?" I'm afraid I'll forget what I want to ask her. If I'm not back for lunch, Mother will know I left, and who knows what will happen if she finds out.

Miss Sandy asks, "Are you doing okay, child?"

I want to ask her when I'll get home, but I don't want the other kids to hear me because when I ask the teacher anything in school, the kids laugh at me, so I just nod.

Miss Sandy touches my hand on my knee. I close my eyes, trying to back away as far as possible without falling out of my seat. I'm expecting to feel pain at any moment like I do when Mother reaches for my hand.

Nothing happens. I open them, and she is staring at me.

She leans closer and whispers, "I'm not going to hurt you, Sarah." I want to believe her because she seems nice.

She brushes my bangs back from my forehead. "How old are you, child?"

"I'm almost nine." A few weeks ago, when Daddy and I worked on a truck together, he'd said, "For a young lady who is almost nine years old, you sure know a lot about trucks."

"I don't know much about churches, though," I tell Miss Sandy.

"You're going to love it."

I hope so. I continue staring out the front window at all the houses we're passing. Some homes look huge, like the size of my school or the grocery store. My house could fit inside of them. Their yards and driveways are long, without junk metal piled everywhere or broken-down cars like mine.

Suddenly, the bus comes to a stop in the middle of the road. My school bus only stops at the sign on the corner, so I look around.

"Why did the bus come to a stop in the middle of the road?"

Miss Sandy shows me what she calls a traffic light, pointing to the tall yellow box with three different-colored lights hanging from a wire in front of the bus. She also goes on to tell me what each light means.

I don't understand the yellow light, but before I ask her about it, I spot a big yellow letter "M" on top of a tall pole. I've never seen anything like it before.

"I bet you like McDonald's, don't you, Sarah?" Miss Sandy asks.

McDonald's? What's in a McDonald's, and why would I like it? I learned that if I shrug when adults ask me questions when I don't know the answer, they stop asking them. It seems to work now with Miss Sandy, who is studying me.

I stare out the front window, pretending not to notice that she and Dave are looking at each other with a sad face. I hope they're not upset with me for not knowing about McDonald's.

The bus starts moving again. Miss Sandy and Dave are no longer looking at each other, which is good because Dave must drive the bus that moves faster as we fly past stores and houses again.

Not far past the big "M," we pull into this huge parking lot in front of a humongous building with a pointy top. It has large, gray rocks stuck all over it except the windows, which have many different colors. They kinda look like a scribbled mess that Emma would do.

It has super-tall, jagged pieces sticking out of the top, which reminds me of the shattered glass in our grass at home from the broken junk-car windows.

I duck down in the seat to get a good look out the window all the way to the top of the building. *Whoa! It's so tall, it almost touches the clouds!*

There are two pieces of wood sticking out the top that crisscross. I almost fall out of my seat.

No! No, no, no! It's a *math* sign!

Why did I come here? I *hate* math. If I knew we would do math, I would never have agreed to go to this place. Oh, why didn't I ask more questions before I decided to come here?

I say nothing out loud, but inside my head, I'm screaming, *I don't want to be here; I don't want to be here!*

Get me outta here!

Chapter 9
Barefoot & Like it or Not

Real shoes! Not only am I wearing dirty,
old clothes covered in mud stains,
but I'm barefoot! Can this day get any worse?

Miss Sandy turns toward me, "Well, Sarah, we're here and it's time to get off the bus." I think about asking her if it could take me home, but then I see all the other kids standing up. Most of them are nicely dressed. Miss Sandy, too, looks really nice with a pretty blue dress that goes to the floor. She wears pink socks, the color of her lips, and black shoes peeking out from under her long dress.

Shoes!

Not only am I wearing dirty, old clothes covered in mud stains, but I'm barefoot! Can this day get any worse?

As I look at my shoeless feet stained dark-brown- paneling color from this morning's mud pies, Miss Sandy checks them out.

We slowly raise our heads to look at one another, "Let's get off this bus so you can get a better look at the church from the parking lot," she says.

We step off, and my eyes go to the church's top. I push my dark ringlets, which have a mind of their own, out of my eyes as I tip my head back to get a better look at the plus sign.

Miss Sandy asks, "Would you like to take my hand or just walk next to me?"

I reach with my hand slowly toward her. It feels like it's moving in slow motion. She closes hers around mine, and we walk into the building together. "If you think the outside is beautiful, Sarah, wait until you see the inside."

As we enter the math building, people are heading toward an enormous room where music plays. This is going to be okay since I love music. As I do in school, I'll just ask to go to the bathroom when math class starts.

Miss Sandy leads me inside a big kitchen where many people get a meal ready.

"Why are people cooking food?"

"Because after church today, there'll be a luncheon for the choir." I don't understand what a choir is, but I nod anyway.

She pats the countertop next to the sink. "Jump up here, Sarah."

My heart does a little happy flip. I feel like I do when Daddy puts me on the sink at home while I help him shave. "Let's wash your feet and legs." Miss Sandy's voice is quiet but sweet.

"Okay," I say just as softly.

Miss Sandy walks across the room to a drawer and rummages through it. While I wait for her, the people in the room say hello, and tell me their names. I hope to remember them all. Everyone seems so nice. *But what'll happen when we have to start doing math and reading like in school?* Maybe I made a mistake coming here. There were questions that Miss Sandy asked me on the bus that I couldn't answer. She was friendly about it, but what if the teacher isn't? Or what if the other kids laugh?

Miss Sandy returns with a white towel while a man in a black suit and white tie comes into the room. His short blond hair is spiky at the ends and sticks straight up like it's combed to go that way. When he stops in front of me, I lower my gaze to the floor. "Hello, Miss Sarah; I'm the Pastor here."

I hold in a giggle because Pastor is a funny name, and I've never heard it before. I look up, saying, "Hi." The Pastor smiles before I focus on my feet again. Miss Sandy has wet the towel with warm water in the large metal sink next to me.

The steam from the hot water is rising in the air right next to where I am sitting, and it feels like it is trying to grab and pull me in.

All of a sudden, *I am back in the bathroom with Mother.*

The steam from the hot water is covering the mirror, making it hard to see me.

Just then, a dish hit the floor, dropped by the woman standing over the stove. I must get away from what she is about to do to me.

61

I jump off the sink. "I don't need to have my feet clean; I can go outside and wait for the bus to leave if I can't go into the math building with no shoes on." "Sweet child, it's okay." I was already off the counter, standing on the floor, ready to leave this building before she finished her words. "Child, you are shaking," she said as she touched my shoulder with her hand. "Honey, I won't hurt you. Are you afraid of the water?" She followed my gaze to the sink. I say nothing but nod my head. "I promise you—I won't hurt you. I'm only going to take this warm cloth to clean your feet."

She takes the warm towel out of the sink. "Feel this, Sarah, so you can see that it is not hot." I take my hand and put it on the towel with a lot of steam coming from it. I stop and close my eyes as I reach to touch it. "Child?" I open my eyes to see my hand on the towel. "Are you okay, honey?" Again, I nod my head. She pats the counter for me to jump back up. I didn't even notice the strange man called Pastor was watching us.

I find my seat back on the counter, and Miss Sandy uses the towel to wash my feet. I didn't know warm water could feel good.

When she finishes, the white towel is the color of my mud pies.

"Wait here a minute, okay, Sarah?" I nod, and then Miss Sandy and Pastor walk away from me, though they are still close enough to hear a little of what they're saying. "What do you suppose just happened back there?" Miss Sandy opens her mouth, but before she speaks, Pastor keeps talking. "Do her parents know she is here?"

"Her father was working in the garage and waved goodbye to us when she got on the bus."

Pastor nods, patting Miss Sandy's arm. "We can talk later." Then, as he walks past me, he says, "Nice to meet you, Sarah. See you soon." And then, just like that, he leaves the kitchen.

I turn back to find Miss Sandy, who is now looking in a closet in the corner. After a few minutes, she walks back with bright pink, fuzzy slippers.

Pink is usually too girly for me, but as she slips them onto my feet, the slippers are so comfortable that I don't care. "Wow, these things are soft."

"I'm glad you like them. That's better, now, isn't it?"

"Sure is."

Miss Sandy digs in her purse. She pulls out a couple of metal pieces that look like nails from the garage at home. I lean back as she brings them closer to my face, worried she might try to stab me with them.

"It won't hurt, Sarah. It'll help keep your hair from covering your beautiful brown eyes."

Sitting still is hard when shiny, sharp things are coming closer and closer to my head. Finally, she slides the metal across my hair on either side. She was right; it didn't hurt one bit. I wonder if Daddy can make some hair slides like these from scrap metal in his garage.

"Wow, my hair isn't moving." I shake my head back and forth and Miss Sandy laughs. "No child, it is keeping your hair out of your face, so this way you can see me and everyone else." She winks with both eyes, one at a time, going back and forth really fast. I try this trick. We both start laughing together because all I could do was scrunch up my face and close both eyes at the same time.

"Okay, Sarah, you're all ready for church if you want to hop down from the counter now."

I do as Miss Sandy says and feel the fuzziness and warmth of the slippers against my feet as I land on the hard floor. I kinda like this feeling, even though I will always like going barefoot best of all.

She leads me out of the kitchen and down a long hallway toward the open, wooden, double doors. The closer we get to the doorway, the louder the pretty music.

Two people stand in front of each open door and hand everyone who enters a paper with a picture and words.

Pastor, standing just inside the doorway says, "Well, hello, Miss Sarah. We meet again. Welcome to our church."

"I am looking forward to worship, Pastor Scott. Is your lovely wife Lisa singing for us this morning?" "Why, yes she is, Sandy." "Oh, Sarah you are in for a treat, wait 'til you hear Pastor Scott's wife, Lisa sing." Miss Sandy announces in a loud excited voice. I skip over the singing part and ask, "Is his name Pastor or Scott?"

"Dear child, good question. His name is Scott, but because he preaches at this church, we call him Pastor Scott."

"Pastor? Preaches? What do those words mean?" I ask.

She smiles. "He's called a pastor because he's the one who teaches us all about the Bible." *There's that word Bible again.*

Miss Sandy stops talking as we go through the big doors. The room suddenly opens up, and the ceiling is so tall that I have to tip my head back to see its top. This is the biggest and tallest room I've ever seen.

When I lower my head, there are rows and rows of what look like very long benches made of thick, dark pieces of wood that go from one side of the building to the other. Miss Sandy leads me to one of the benches. We stand in front of it instead of sitting on it. She removes a book from the bench in front of us, opens it, then sings along with the rest of the people.

The most beautiful windows I've ever seen are on either side of us. Now that I see them from the inside, I realize they aren't scribbles but pictures of different people I don't know. One is of a man carrying a big, wooden math sign on his back, and he has pricker bushes in a circle on his head. Man, those prickers would hurt; I know how much they hurt when they scratch up my legs.

The music stops, then we all sit down. Pastor Scott stands at the front on a step and says loudly, "I would like to welcome new members to our church family today. I would also like to announce that my wife, Lisa, will help me deliver our worship message this morning." As Pastor Scott speaks, a lady next to him waves at us. I'm about to wave back, but no one else does, so I keep my hand down.

As Pastor Scott talks, he raises his hands into the air. Everyone else does too. "Sarah, raise your hands in the air like me," she whispers.

Why? Is something going to drop from the ceiling? Candy? That would be fantastic!

But nothing happens, and everyone just drops their hands for no reason at all. So I don't understand any of it.

Next, all the kids walk to the front of the room to stand in front of Pastor Scott and his wife, Miss Lisa, who then hold their hands over the kids' heads.

Pastor Scott and Miss Lisa are going to hit them! I push my teeth together, and my jaw gets really tight.

Trying to hide, I sink onto the bench. That pastor better not ask me to come up front to get hit too. I really want to be home right now. These kids are crazy! They're just standing there, looking happy. Why did I come here? I could be home making mud pies or helping Daddy in the garage. Why did Daddy let me come here? This seems more like a place Mother would want me to go than Daddy.

But then Pastor Scott and Miss Lisa begin to sing a song about the word Bible.

"B.I.B.L.E, yes, that's the book for me, I stand alone on the word of God, the B.I.B.L.E."

The kids sing along with them, looking happy, and not one of them has been hit.

Miss Sandy whispers, "Sarah, walk up and stand with the rest of the kids so you can go with them."

My mouth opens. I don't want to go. I don't want to stand in front of a bunch of people I don't know and have the kids laugh at me. But how do I tell Miss Sandy *no* when she's been so nice?

Pastor Scott continues to hold his hands above the kids as I walk up. Aren't his arms getting tired yet? I guess he'll drop them after he hits all of them. I stand behind the kids in case the pastor and his wife change their minds and start hitting.

One of the girls grabs my hand and pulls me to stand next to her. She is little like me, so I don't mind.

There's a lady playing music on the piano, and everyone starts to sing. Except for me. And when some of the kids see that I'm not singing, they elbow each other and laugh.

I put my head down. This is what I thought would happen and why I didn't want to walk up here in the first place. I will not stand here and let these kids laugh at me. Just then, the girl squeezes my hand. "Pretend to sing."

I don't know how to do that, so I put my head down.

Then, Pastor Scott begins to talk about God. He calls church, "God's house."

I've met many people today, and even though I'm worried about forgetting everyone's name, I'm sure I would remember the name God if I had met him.

The pastor tells God to protect us and says we should, "Go with God."

I keep looking around the room for God, but I don't know what he looks like.

And where are we going with God? I haven't met this God person yet, and I'm not supposed to go places with strangers.

The kids begin to move, walking in a single file line. Why are these adults just sitting here allowing this God person to take us? Why is God only taking the kids? Where are we going? I want to scream and run back to Miss Sandy or out through the double doors and keep running until I'm home.

I look at Miss Sandy once more. She nods and smiles at me. I feel a little better after that, but I'm still so confused. Why did I get on that bus? Busses take me to places I don't like to go.

Then Pastor Scott says, "Dear God, our Savior, please take these children under your wing to help them learn all they can this morning."

Take us? That's it. I need to get out of here!

I turn to run out of the building, but as I look at the adults and the kids again, I see that everyone seems fine, and most are smiling.

Maybe I'm wrong about this God person. Maybe I should let him take me—it'll be better than getting laughed at if I run away.

So, I guess I'm going with God today, whether I like it or not.

Chapter 10
The Picture & Learning to Pray

"Sarah? Sarah, do you like that picture?" she asks. I don't answer. "Sarah…? Sarah…?" The teacher sits down next to me as she says my name repeatedly. "Do you know who that is in the picture, Sarah?" I continue to stare at the picture and slowly shake my head.

"Welcome to Sunday school, Sarah."

That stops me dead in my tracks. *School*?

I go into a room that looks like a classroom. Decorations are hung everywhere, but tables and chairs are sitting around the room instead of desks.

What's going on? Why am I stuck in a place just like school, feeling just as stupid? Once again, I'm the dummy, showing up dirty with no shoes and clueless. I want to leave.

"Everyone, please take your seat so we can get the class started." I knew it. I knew this was just like my other school. I need to get out of here.

"I want to go back out and sit with Miss Sandy," I tell her as she stands next to me. "Sarah, could you hang out here for a little while? We're going to be doing some fun activities. If, after ten minutes, you still want to find Sandy, I'll walk you back to the congregation to find her. Is that okay?"

The teacher talks to me so nicely that I make up my mind to stay. Besides, the rest of the kids listen and watch us, so I just stay put. But I'm still so angry with myself for coming here that I'm stewing—which is what Mother says I'm doing when I'm mad.

I'm stuck here until Dave takes us home. I walk toward an empty table to take a seat.

"Hey, Sarah," says the girl who held my hand. "Come sit with Jackie and me. My name is Debbie." She pats an empty chair between them. Jackie reminds me of a Barbie® doll a girl at school had brought in for show-and-tell.

Mille Frank had made fun of me for not knowing what the doll was called and not having one of my own. "Everyone has a Barbie® doll," she'd announced when I'd asked her about it. That's what Jackie looks like with long blonde hair and huge, dark-blue eyes.

"Why don't you have shoes on?" Jackie asks me.

"I forgot to put them on before I got on the bus. I was outside my house making mud pies when the bus pulled up and asked me to go to church, so I just got on without my shoes." It's so easy to talk to this girl. I'm usually very quiet around new people, afraid they will laugh at me.

Jackie's eyes get big. "That's so cool. I love to play in the mud too. Debbie doesn't." Jackie pointed her thumb at her friend. "She's too girlygirl."

"Yeah, well, I can jump rope longer and faster than you can, Jackie." Debbie sticks out her tongue.

"It doesn't matter how fast you are at jump rope because I can run faster than you!" Jackie crosses her arms with a nod.

"This is going to be fun, Sarah, you'll see," Debbie whispers to me, ignoring what Jackie just said to her.

I sigh. How will this school be different from my other one, where the work is hard, and the kids are mean?

The teacher hands each of us a black book with tiny pages and writing. The words next to the numbers look even bigger than the list of spelling words we're supposed to know for school. Then the teacher assigns us each a part.

My turn to read comes.

My heart is pounding through my chest, and I feel I can't take a deep breath. It gets faster and faster to where I feel like I'm panting like Maisy does when she's hot. The words look like they are disappearing on the page right before me. My hands start shaking, and I have sweat rolling down my back under my shirt.

What is going on?

I can't breathe.

Sarah just read it, I tell myself, and then I begin. It's *so* hard. I'm messing up a lot, and some kids are making fun of me. When I finish, I raise my head and can tell their laughing at *me*. The teacher tries to shush them.

Thankfully, the laughing stops as I put my head down.

The next person is reading when I walk to the back table in the corner of the room, just like I do in school when I want to be alone. I sit down and keep my head on my arm, facing the wall, lying on the table. I try to swallow the lump stuck in my throat that always comes when I feel embarrassed.

The class stops reading. "Teacher, can we sit with Sarah?" Debbie and Jackie say at the same time, like they practiced it.

"Thank you, girls, but I'll go to Sarah," the Sunday school teacher says as she walks around the room, handing things out to the other kids. She tells them a story about Moses floating in a basket down the River Nile.

The story is nice because a lady at the river saved him from the water, taking him home to be her baby. But I want to learn more when she says, "Color your pictures of Moses now, children."

Though I enjoy coloring, I don't stay inside the lines.

"Sarah, can I join you?"

I lift my head and look up at the teacher, who is now standing over me.

"Sarah, can I sit with you a second?" Before nodding, I look around the room, hoping the other kids aren't watching. But instead, I can see they're all busy coloring and fighting over crayons. Debbie and Jackie look up for a few seconds in my direction, then go back to what they were doing.

When I turn around from the class, it's then I spot the picture on the wall behind the teacher. It's a photo of a man with wavy light brown hair down to his shoulders and a brown beard. The teacher is talking to me, but it's as if she's very far away. The guy in this picture looks right at me!

The lump in my throat starts to go away.

The teacher watches me for a second, then her head turns to face the picture on the wall. Now we both are looking at the same image. Then, sitting down in a seat next to me, she asks, "Sarah, do you like that picture?"

I don't answer because I am too busy staring at it. The man smiles and has green eyes like I've never seen, not even like Mama Cat.

I swear I know him, or I've seen him before, but where? Maybe I saw him in Daddy's garage? Perhaps Daddy and I have painted his car together. So many of Daddy's customers say hi to me when they see me.

Why do I know him?

Do I know him?

"Sarah...? Sarah...?" The teacher leans closer to me as she says my name over and over. "Do you know who that is in the picture, Sarah?" The picture?

I can't turn away. Slowly I shake my head and say, "I don't think so, but I'm not sure. I kinda think Daddy and I painted a car for him before."

"I don't think that's possible Sarah because that is Jesus." I say nothing, keeping my eyes on the painting. "Do you know who Jesus is?

Have you ever heard of him before?" I shake my head.

"Let me tell you about Him," she says.

I don't turn away from the picture while she's speaking. Then, when she stops talking, I ask,

"His name is Jesus? Why is he staring at me?" She answers all my questions, just like Daddy.

"Jesus sees everything."

My eyes bug out. "Jesus sees *everything*?"

"Yes, Sarah. He sees everything."

When she tells me this news, I turn away from the picture of Jesus and look in her direction.

"Did you ever pray before?" she asks.

"Pray? What's that?" Quickly, I make sure no one is listening to us. "Could I show you how to do it?"

I'm not sure I want to learn how to pray, since I have no idea what it is, or why I would want to in the first place.

But before I can answer, she says, "You can pray to Jesus anytime, anywhere, Sarah, and he will hear you. Jesus loves everyone, and children are special to him. He loves everything in this world, including animals."

"Jesus is like me as I love all animals too. But why would Jesus love me if he doesn't know me?"

"Oh, he knows you, Sarah. When you feel scared and all alone, Jesus is there with you. You are never alone. In his eyes, you are beautiful and loved by him."

"Even with my big eyebrows and buck teeth?"

"Yes, Jesus loves everything about you."

"If I am scared, I can pray to him, and I'm not alone anymore?"

"Yes, Sarah, though you can't see him, he will be there with you."

'So, Jesus is like magic?"

She snickers, "Yes, he is like magic. He can hear you wherever you are."

"How can he hear me?"

"Because he can hear everyone," the teacher speaks to me quietly. This is so weird. Why hasn't Daddy told me about this magic Jesus? He tells me everything.

"The Bible tells us stories about Jesus coming to earth and sent by God, His Father." "But who is this God person? Do you mean he's not *really* going to take all the kids anywhere?"

"No, Sarah, that's just a saying we use, meaning to go with God and believe in Him."

Phew. That makes me feel better.

"He died for our sins because he loves us all so very much," she exclaims with a gigantic smile.

I frown. "He died?"

"Yes, but he did it for you, for me, for all of us. And don't worry, Sarah, he doesn't stay dead."

Whoa, just like Lucky! I guess I should be happy he did it for me, but I still don't understand why he had to die. I'm confused and excited at the same time. Daddy loves me, but he's the only one who does. Now I have Jesus, and he loves me, too.

"Having faith is believing in what you cannot see," she says.

"This will be hard for me," I tell her, "but I'll try."

"My sweet Sarah, Jesus has a plan for us all."

I move to the edge of my seat. "What's his plan for me, teacher?"

"We'll eventually find out His plan for us by praying and believing in Him," she says, then shows me how to pray.

A few other kids watch us, but no one says anything mean.

"Can I show you quick how to say a prayer?" I nod.

"Let's put our hands together." She shows me how to lock my fingers together, and then she closes her eyes so I know to close mine. "Dear Jesus, I would like you to meet your child, Sarah. She learned all about you today for the first time. I told her you would always be with her in her times of sadness, happiness and when she is afraid. We are teaching her to pray right now. Please always stand by her and protect her as she goes through her life journey. In Jesus name I pray, Amen."

After saying the prayer, the teacher opens her eyes and looks at me. "See, Sarah? That's how you do it. Before you go to bed each night, kneel by your bed, lace your hands together like I did, and talk to Jesus. Though He cannot answer you the way other people do, He can hear you. You have to believe, Sarah. Just believe, and He will be there for you." The teacher reaches over and gives me a hug. I didn't know what to do. I never had anyone hug me except Daddy.

After letting go of me, she says, "Sarah, how about we go back and sit with the rest of the class? That way, we can have everyone pray together?"

I nod and head back to Debbie and Jackie.

The teacher laces her hands together, and the rest of us imitate her as we lower our heads and close our eyes.

"Jessica, can you start our closing prayer?" the teacher asks.

Jessica agrees so cheerfully that I figure she must really love praying. "Dear Jesus, please keep us safe as we leave Sunday school and the church today. Oh, and please watch over us in school this week."

"Thank you, Jessica. I will close our prayer before you all leave to head back with your families."

I keep my hands crisscrossed and my eyes closed as the teacher talks to Jesus.

"Dear Jesus, please protect these children and their families wherever they go. Give us the strength to follow your lead in everything we do. Let them show other children how to obey and believe in you, Lord. Amen."

Everyone says "Amen" after the teacher says it. Then, a boy with brown hair, brown eyes, and even tanner skin than mine raises his hand.

"Yes, Ed?"

"And I hope that no one makes fun of anyone at Sunday school class anymore." He smiles at me and then quickly looks down.

"That was lovely, Ed, thank you. Yes, children, I hope you will remember to be kind to everyone."

We end our time in Sunday school singing a song I will never forget called "Jesus Loves Me." No one has a music book in front of them, but they all know the words. I listen carefully.

> *Jesus loves me this, I know, for the Bible tells me so,*
> *little ones to Him belong,*
> *they are weak, but He is strong.*
> *Yes, Jesus loves me. Yes, Jesus loves me.*
> *Yes, Jesus loves me; the Bible tells me so.*

The class sings it three times before the group leader knocks on the door. "We are ready for you to return to the main room for the closing message." Even after the singing is over, I can't stop thinking about the words.

Jesus loves me. Jesus loves *me.* When I sing those words with everyone else, I feel something inside me that I can't explain.

We walk back to the room where the adults are sitting. The teacher walks out beside me. It feels like a lot of people are watching as we walk into that huge room again. Then, a disaster happens when my foot slips out of the pink fuzzy slipper, but the teacher stops so I can put it back onto my foot.

Once I'm done, I notice Pastor Scott and his wife singing together. There's beautiful music, and I stop and listen to Miss Lisa sing because she sounds just like Dolly Parton. I bet Daddy would love to come here and listen to her since he loves Dolly Parton.

While I watch Miss Lisa, she looks right at me and waves. I wave back, smiling.

"Hey, Sarah, let's keep moving so we can all find our seats," the teacher says. "We're holding up the line."

Miss Sandy stands up so I can find her among all the people. I cannot wait to tell her everything I've done and learned. Just when I reach the row she is sitting in, everyone shouts, "Amen!" and I jump. I know that word now. That's the word we say when we're done talking to Jesus.

As I sit down next to Miss Sandy, the pastor is still talking, so I have to be quiet for now. I see Jesus in one of the pretty, colored windows. My hand slaps over my mouth. Jesus is the guy with the round prickers on his head carrying the big math sign on his back! *Poor Jesus.*

When we walk outside toward the blue bus, Debbie, Jackie, and Ed walk by with their parents. I'm surprised when they yell, "Goodbye, Sarah! See you next Sunday!"

"Bye!" I yell and wave at the same time. Do I have friends now? I hope I will see them next Sunday.

I climb up the steps and get into the same seat as before— only, this time, my seat is next to the window.

As I begin to tell Miss Sandy about Sunday school, I realize I didn't learn my teacher's name. Pressing my face up against the bus window, I spot her.

If only I could make this bus stop so I can hop off, hug her again, and thank her for teaching me about God and Jesus. Instead, I wave goodbye.

Next week seems so far away. I cannot *wait* for the teacher to teach me more about Jesus.

I'm so, so happy I got on the blue bus.

Wait, what is Mother going to do when I get home? I completely lost track of time. How long have I been at church? It's impossible to see the sun behind all the clouds while sitting on the bus.

If Mother already called me for lunch and I'm not there, I don't want to think about what will happen.

What is Mother going to do to me?

Chapter 11
Snakes & Answered Prayers

"You're gonna get eaten by a big ole rattlesnake.
Curtis, when you go to bed.
It's going to come in through your bedroom window, and sink its
poisonous fangs in you, and hopefully kill both of you."

I slide the slippers off my feet when Miss Sandy waves her hand at me. "No, Sarah, these are a gift from me to you. You can wear them to church next Sunday."

Already sick with worry about getting punished for missing lunch, the thought of taking these slippers to my house, and Mother seeing them, makes me look at my hands and imagine the blisters all over them. "Oh, there's no way I can take these slippers home. If Mother sees them, she'll know I left the house without telling her and without my shoes." Miss Sandy frowns at Dave.

"We saw your dad wave at you as we were pulling away," Dave says. "Wouldn't he have told her where you run off to?"

"I don't think so." I rock back and forth while confessing my other worry to them. "I think I missed lunch, too."

Miss Sandy tilts her head. "Well, unless you eat before noon, Sarah, you probably didn't miss lunch."

But I'm still sure Mother has been calling and looking for me and is very mad. Just thinking about having to see Mother after she's been looking for me has my stomach twisting like a snake.

"As for your slippers," Sandy says, "maybe you could put them in one of the cars out front for safekeeping?"

"That's a great idea."

"Why don't you take your mind off your slippers and missing lunch and tell me all about Sunday school?"

Still concerned about Mother but unable to hide my excitement, I ask her, "Miss Sandy, did you know Jesus loves *me*?" I can barely sit in my seat; I'm so eager to talk about it.

She sits up straight and claps her hands together. "Of course, Jesus loves you, dear." She pats my knee, and this time, I don't close my eyes and back away because I know she won't hurt me. "Would you like to go to church next Sunday?"

"Yes, very much!" I can't contain myself and bounce on the seat.

We make a few stops along the way to drop off other kids. Some of their houses look a lot nicer than mine. One boy gets off the bus, and *both* his mom and dad are in the driveway waiting for him with their dog and a pretty little girl—probably his sister. They hug him as soon as he gets off the bus, and you can tell the dog is happy to see him, too, because he jumps on him. Then, as the bus pulls away, they all walk up the driveway with their arms around him.

My family doesn't act that way. Well, except for Daddy.

When we stop at the traffic light, this green station wagon has happy people inside. It's a warm day, so the bus windows are open, and all three beautiful girls in the back are laughing.

The boy's sister was pretty. The girls in the station wagon are too. Even Debbie and Jackie are pretty. And they all look so happy. If only *I* was pretty, maybe kids would stop picking on me, and I could be happy.

Maybe I can pray about that.

I can't kneel because there's not enough room, so I lean my head against the window and close my eyes.

"Dear Jesus, it's me, Sarah. We just met a little while ago at God's house. I came there on a blue bus. The Sunday school teacher told me all about you and how to talk to you after I saw that picture of you on the wall. She told me you'll listen to me if I believe in you and pray to you. So, let's make a deal. I swear I'll believe in you my whole life no matter what anyone else tries to tell me if you give me two eyebrows instead of this one big one, two straight teeth that are not broken and don't stick out from my lips, and just, well, make me pretty so people stop making fun of me. And *please* make my family happy like those other two families I just saw out this window. Oh, and sorry about the pricker bush on your head. I know how much that must've hurt. Amen."

I open my eyes, and Miss Sandy watches me with tears running down her face. Just then, it hits me—I'd said my prayer out loud. I wonder why she's so sad.

With her hand over her heart, she leans close to me. "Sweet girl, I believe Jesus heard your prayer and that your life will be exactly the way you want it to be. Just have faith, Miss Sarah. Just keep the faith."

I nod, remembering that the teacher at Sunday school told me to have faith, too.

Before I know it, we're stopped in front of my house. I stand up to leave the bus, and my face changes from happy to frightened instantly.

Miss Sandy stands and opens her arms.

I hug her back. I don't remember the last time anyone hugged me except for Daddy, and now I got two of them in one day.

"Goodbye Sarah, it was so nice to meet you." Dave gives me a high-five as I walk past him and get off the bus.

Before I walk down the steps, I turn to Miss Sandy and say, "How will I know when it's Sunday and what time the blue bus will come to my house?" "Ask your parents, child. I'm sure they will tell you." "Okay, maybe, I'll ask my Daddy to help me." "Wouldn't your mother remind you when it is Sunday?" I stand at the top of the steps looking at Miss Sandy, before I speak again, not knowing what to say. "Mother is too busy to help me with something like that. But Daddy will."

I'm thankful to Miss Sandy for giving me another great idea and skipping down the steps and off the bus. I wave at Dave, Miss Sandy, and the other kids and then head up the driveway to tell Daddy everything.

He's in the garage with the torch lit as he's still welding. As I start up the middle of the driveway, I realize Mother might see me coming through the small kitchen window. So I change direction and walk up the right side of the driveway on the other side of all the cars along the creek where Mother can't see me. I've already taken off my slippers, carrying them in my hand. Not only am I being careful that Mother won't see me wearing them, but I'm also holding them, so I can't ruin them walking through the tall grass.

My stomach makes hungry noises. I look up at the sky and notice the sun is where it usually is when I'm supposed to go in for lunch. It feels like I've been gone all day, but maybe Miss Sandy is right.

I run really fast into the garage, but I stop quickly and walk over to Daddy once I get inside. *Safety first, I'm gonna be safe.* I sing like Dolly Parton inside my head.

Daddy stops welding right away. He sets down his tools, steps away from his work, and opens his arms for a hug.

I run to him, and he picks me up, swinging me around in a circle with my legs flying through the air.

He kisses my cheek and listens to my story of adventure.

"They want me to come back next Sunday. Can I please? Can I? They told me they'd pick me up again at the end of the driveway. Can you help me figure out what day is Sunday and what time I should wait for the bus, Daddy?"

"Why, of course, Dolly."

I hug him even tighter than before. "Oh, thank you, thank you! I knew I could count on you!"

Then he asks, "What do you have there in your hands? Something pink?"

My face gets hot because I'm worried about Mother seeing me with these slippers. I'd been so excited to talk to Daddy and worried that Mother saw me that I forgot to hide them in one of the old cars like Miss Sandy said.

Daddy sees the look on my face and quickly says, "Remember, I told you, there's nothing wrong with being a girl, and pink matches your pretty little cheeks." He kisses each one of them again.

"It's not because the slippers are pink; I'm scared about what Mother will do if she finds out I left today. She'll be angry because I forgot my shoes and Miss Sandy gave me these slippers."

Daddy winks. "Let's put them in this drawer in your workbench, Dolly. No one ever goes in there. When it's Sunday and you need to wait for the bus, you can come in here and get your slippers then head to the top of the driveway. No one will ever know except for you and me." "And Jesus!" I add.

"And Jesus," Daddy agrees with a chuckle.

He reaches up, and I feel the pins Miss Sandy put in my hair sliding out. He sticks them in the drawer with the slippers. "I like seeing your pretty eyes, Dolly, but we best put those in with the slippers as well."

I smile at Daddy just as my hair, once again, falls in front of my eyes. "Maybe you could make me some of those from your scrap metal, Daddy? They worked great."

He chuckles again. "Maybe I can make you something like that, Dolly."

Remembering a few more details about my day that I'm just getting ready to tell Daddy, I hear Mother scream from the porch, "Git in the house for lunch, Sarah."

"Coming, Mother!" Miss Sandy was right about the time.

"When you're done eating lunch, come back out to the garage so you can help me tape off a car and get it ready for painting."

I yell over my shoulder as I race from the garage to the house, "Okay, Daddy! See you soon!"

When I get inside, Curtis is already at the table, eating lunch. I have a whole peanut butter and jelly sandwich, not just half of one today. *Wow!* First, Sunday school and Jesus, then I make it back in time for lunch, and Mother doesn't even know I left. Daddy hides my slippers and metal slides for me and will let me help him in the garage after lunch. Today might be the best day of my life because all my favorite things happen all at once.

I'm able to sneak out to the garage before Mother scolds me for bothering Daddy. We spend the entire afternoon listening to all kinds of music on his 8-track player, singing the songs while we tape off and start spraying the car he's been hired to repaint. Time goes by so fast when I help Daddy.

Daddy tells me once we clean everything up, "Head into the house and let your mother know I'll be in shortly." My thumb is in the air before sprinting out of the garage and into the house.

I come inside to find Curtis sitting on the floor, watching television. Derek's sitting on the couch with Vinnie. I look in the playpen for Emma. I thought I would read an animal book to her, but the playpen is empty. "Mother, where's Emma?" "What does it matter to ya?" she responded using her grumpy voice. "I wanted to read her a storybook." "Well, ya can't 'cause Vinnie took her to Christy's house because she's watchin' her tonight." Being afraid stops me in my tracks like the pricker bushes Daddy calls horse nettle. They wrap around your ankles and cut into you if you try to move. I told Daddy that I loved horses, but I sure hated their pricker bushes. I forgot all about Mother asking him to babysit us last night.

Derek smirks while saying, "Yup, me and the boys are watching you kiddies tonight."

Daddy comes in and heads for the bathroom. Before he gets through the living room, he looks over his shoulder and says, "Hey there, Dolly. Are you coming to help me shave or what?"

My feet start to work, and I walk into the bathroom to watch him. Today I don't sit on the sink but on the toilet lid behind him. He says he needs to do the shaving himself tonight to get ready for their anniversary.

Skip the anniversary, I want to tell him. *Please* don't leave us with the boys, especially Derek. If only I could tell Daddy how scared I am of Derek, but Daddy looks like he's excited about going out with Mother tonight. Even when they go out for bingo, Daddy doesn't look this happy. He's only this happy when working in the garage or when I make him smile and laugh.

"Daddy, can I go to Christy's house with Emma? I can help Christy watch her and bring books to read to her?" "No, Dolly. Vinnie has already left to take Emma over there. Besides, you need to stay here with Curtis," Daddy says while messing up my hair with his hand.

"Could you and Mother drop me off on your way out on your anniversary?" Daddy stops putting his shaving cream on his face and looks at me. "We aren't going in the same direction to where your sister Christy lives, or we would've dropped Emma off ourselves. It would be way out of our way. Plus, Curtis likes it when you're with him. Maybe you two could come up with some games to play tonight?" Just then, he takes some shaving cream and puts a dot of it on the end of my nose. Oh, we'll be playing games tonight, except they aren't games that Curtis and I come up with to play. If only he knew that the game, we will play tonight is why I am trying to figure out a way to get out of here. But he's right. I couldn't leave Curtis here alone.

Daddy finishes shaving, and we head back out into the living room. Mother doesn't cook tonight since she and Daddy are going out to dinner before they go dancing. "Derek, give 'um somethin' to eat, okay?" "Yeah, sure," he tells her.

As soon as Mother and Daddy walk out the door, Derek starts in on Curtis.

"You're gonna get eaten by a big ole rattlesnake, Curtis, when you go to bed. It's gonna come in your room through your bedroom window and sink its poisonous fangs in you and hopefully kill both of you." Derek then turns to scowl at me, waiting for a reaction.

Derek creeps me out and gives me goosebumps when he looks at me. I'm standing there, rocking back and forth as I think about what will happen next.

Then, the phone rings, and Derek answers it. He starts talking really nice to the person on the other end of the line, using a voice I've never heard before.

Vinnie and Terry say he must be talking to a girl, and they start making these smacking sounds with their lips.

Derek makes a face at them and balls up his fist, holding it high in the air. "Shit Vinnie, we are going to get it now," Terry yells.

When my oldest brother Derek makes a fist, you know what's coming. A fight.

Maisy is lying on her rug on the floor in the living room. I lie on the floor too with my feet on the vent. The mornings and nights are starting to get really cold. I lie there, thinking about Mama Cat, Lucky, and the other kittens, and hope they're warm under the car in their bed of hay. Curtis is still watching television. Vinnie and Terry argue about which one of them is the strongest and arm wrestle to decide the answer.

Finally, Derek hangs up the phone.

I try to pretend not to notice and just lie there, hoping to blend into the rust-colored, shaggy carpet, so crushed down in places that it's like the bald spot on our principal's head.

Derek walks over and punches Terry in the face. The crack it makes when his fist meets Terry's cheek makes me duck, as if I were getting hit instead. The second Vinnie hears Terry yelp, he runs into another room. "Get back here, Vinnie; you will help me with these brats. Don't you ever laugh at me again when I'm on the phone because you won't have a chance to run away next time," he yells through the house as he stomps after Vinnie.

When Derek returns, he turns his anger on Curtis and me. "Sarah and Curtis, go to bed now!" We didn't have to be told twice.

Curtis and I jump up and race into the bedroom. Curtis dives onto his bed, and I climb up onto mine as quickly as possible. The bed shakes a little, but I hurry anyway, hoping it doesn't fall on Curtis. I pull my sheet and blanket over myself fast.

Derek follows us into our room, giving us a creepy smile. He shakes Emma's baby rattle at us as he warns, "Sweet dreams. Don't let the rattlesnake's bite! And don't you two dare get out of bed, do you understand me?" He doesn't wait for us to answer but instead yanks the nightlight out of the wall as he stomps across the floor and out of the room.

Our door slides into the wall, and even though it doesn't have a lock on it, we don't dare try to get out after that warning. We haven't had anything to eat and no bath. It's pitch-black in our room, but I'll take that treatment any day over what could've happened.

Curtis is whimpering because he's scared of the dark and the rattlesnake that Derek said would get us tonight. Derek knows I am not afraid of any other snakes except rattlesnakes and that's exactly why he said it would bite us.

"Curtis, stop crying, the rattlesnake won't get you. You don't even have a window by your bed. Plus, how many times have you seen me catch the garter snakes in our yard and at the creek?" Curtis says nothing at first because he is still crying, and then I hear him say, "You pick them up a lot, Sarah, but Derek said rattlesnakes can kill us and come through our bedroom window to bite us." "Curtis, we would hear a rattlesnake coming because they make noise with their tails. So, we would have time to get away from them."

"I wish you had your stick in the house that you use to catch snakes in the yard and creek, Sarah." "Curtis, don't worry, if the rattlesnake comes through my window, it would get me before you."

"I don't want the snake to bite you either Sarah," he cries. "Don't worry about it, my window up here is closed and there is no way for a rattlesnake to get in here, okay?"

I'm not sure he really believes what I told him, but it works as he stops crying. Now, I'm lying here with my stomach rumbling, wide awake, worrying about the rattlesnake coming in and killing us. I lie there for what seems a long time when I hear the door in the living room open and close repeatedly. New voices are in our house. They sound like girls. "Hey, Vinnie, do you have another glass?" And, "Derek, why don't you sit over here next to me?" It's definitely girl's voices, without a doubt.

I look at my window, but it's too dark to see anything. Still, I watch to see if a rattlesnake is about to come inside. Finally, I climb down from my bed, which is even harder to do now with no light to help me see where to step. I just have to feel my way. Finally, I reach the bottom and kneel next to Curtis's bed.

"What're you doing? Derek told us to stay in bed."

"Keep quiet." I close my eyes, put my hands together, and say, "Dear Jesus, you don't really know me, and I don't really know you. We met in the church today, and I talked to you on the blue bus on the way home, remember? Can you hear me okay right now? Well, I sure hope you can because I have to ask you to do something for me. Okay, Jesus, if you're real and you can hear me, I need you to do your magic and make it rain. Okay? Is that a deal? I'm Sarah. I'm nine years old, and I live in this house. Can you see me? Can you hear me, Jesus?" I stop for a few minutes, listening for an answer from Him. All I hear, though, are the boys and whatever they're doing in the living room. They're now playing music. Loudly. I'm worried Jesus won't hear me with all the noise coming from out there.

I close my eyes again, place my hands back together, and add, "Please help me not be afraid of the rattlesnakes. Daddy told me snakes don't like the rain. So, Jesus, I need to ask you a favor again; please make it rain tonight so the rattlesnakes stay under their rocks."

"Sarah, what are you doing on your knees by my bed and who are you talking to?" "Never mind, go to sleep, I'm praying, and I can't stop once I start." Curtis is quiet for a few seconds before his mattress lets me know he is rolling over to face the wall.

I'm getting tired, but I'm so hungry, and it's so dark in here and noisy in the living room that I don't think I'll be able to sleep. Then I think and ask, "If I close my eyes to sleep, why do I close my eyes to talk to you, Jesus? How will I know you see me? I need to ask Miss Sandy or my Sunday school teacher that question since you don't talk. Well, Jesus..." I yawn. "I'll talk to you tomorrow. I'm going to bed now. Please help me. Goodnight, Jesus." I open my eyes and stand up, then quickly drop back down on my knees, close my eyes, fold my hands again, and say, "Amen."

Crawling back up and into my bunk has to happen fast, so Derek doesn't catch me out of bed. Curtis has been quiet for a while now. I can hear him snoring, so I know he's sleeping and on his back.

What's that smell? It smells fantastic! It's food. They're eating something in the living room. Mother's dinners *never* smell this good. The more I lay there, the more my stomach hurts, imagining how yummy that food would taste right now. My mouth fills up with water, but I don't dare get up to go looking for something to eat. If I get caught, I can only imagine what the boys will do to me, and since they're in the living room, I will definitely get caught. Ignoring the noise my stomach makes is getting harder by the second.

The outside door opens and closes a few more times. The music stops, and the voices sound like they are far away now. I try to close my eyes. They feel heavy, and I yawn a little more, but I can't sleep. I'm hungry and being scared about rattlesnakes is keeping me awake. I think about the song the Sunday school teacher taught me and sing it quietly over and over until it's no longer coming from my mouth but playing inside my head, and I fall fast asleep.

I wake to Mother yelling at us to get ready for school in the morning.

People are walking back and forth through our room.

Mother hollers, "Move, you two."

Curtis squirms out from under his covers, gets off the bed, and runs into the bathroom.

Our day starts the same way over and over. I hate it inside my house, but I don't like school either. I'm only happy when I can play outside or help Daddy in the garage. But now I have a new place to be happy… church.

I start the climb down my bunk when I hear something hitting against my window. As I look in that direction, I freeze in place with one foot on the wooden step and the other hanging in the air. It's raining outside! It's raining! It's raining! Jesus *did* hear me, after all!

I can't wait to talk to that guy again tonight!

Chapter 12
POOR & Happy Birthday to Me

*I learned my lesson the hard way about spelling in first grade.
A lot of my papers were marked with POOR. I was told, if the paper
had a word with four letters and two circles in the middle,
it spells GOOD.
One day, I got a math test back with a word written at the top. I'd
counted the letters and looked for the two-letter "O's,"
which I thought meant the word GOOD.
I gave Mother my paper with the four letters and got my face slapped
while she yelled, "And what am I supposed to do with this paper,
Sarah?" She'd waved the paper in my face. "Ya got a paper that says
'POOR' on it? Why aren't ya doin' better in school?
Are ya stupid or what?
POOR means you're stupid."
"Git to your bedroom. There will be no supper for you, Stupid.
That day, I'd learned the difference between a four-letter word that
began with a "P" versus a "G." I never made that mistake again.*

The number one subject I hate in school is math. Number two is spelling.

"Students, listen up. Please remember to take your spelling words home to study tonight for your test on Friday," Mrs. Young says as she passes back our spelling test from last week.

Another POOR.

And it needs to be signed by a parent.

I will not show this test to Mother, because I will get hit for sure if I do.

Mrs. Young walks by my desk as I stand up and sit down for no reason at all. I can't sit down right now while thinking about how I have to take this paper home to Mother.

"Sarah, I need you to sit in your seat and stop fidgeting." I want to tell her that if she doesn't want me to fidget, she shouldn't ask me to take papers home to get them signed, but instead, I just nod as she talks.

Maybe I can leave this paper in my desk like all the others. It's as if Mrs. Young is reading my mind. "We will be cleaning out your desks by the end of class." You gotta be kidding me. Then it gets worse. Mrs. Young announces, "If you don't get your test signed and returned to me, I will have to call home." *What?*

As she promised, we clean our desks. "Can I sit with you for a second?" Mrs. Young pulls over another seat and starts to help me clean. "Well Sarah, you like to save all your work here at school, I see." If only she knew the real story. "Sarah, all these papers are okay to take home. They are not graded." Wow, maybe Mrs. Young did understand what I was doing. "I don't like to take papers home to Mother." "Why Sarah, what happens if you bring home your work that shows you need more practice?" I started, "If the paper says POOR, Mother will…" I change my mind. "Nothing happens. Mother just gets mad."

Mrs. Young leans close to my desk and whispers, "What does Mother do when she gets mad, Sarah?" I put my head down. I say nothing. "Sarah, what does Mother do when she gets mad?" "Nothing. Mother doesn't do anything when she gets mad." "You can tell me anything if you ever need to talk, okay?" My head stays down on my folded arms as I nod. I hear Mrs. Young's chair sliding across the floor, so I sit up. She hands me a stack of wrinkled papers from inside my desk and winks like Daddy. "These are good to take home." When Mrs. Young walks away, I sneak over to the garbage can and throw them all away.

My stomach does flip-flops the whole bus ride home. I sit in my seat with my head against the window, holding my *POOR* spelling test. If only I could throw it out the window.

I sit up straight and tall in my bus seat. *Daddy!* Of course! Why didn't I think of that sooner?

The teacher only said *a* parent had to sign the paper; she didn't say *Mother* had to sign it. Just the thought of showing Daddy my "POOR" paper makes me sad. The only person in my life who tells me I'm smart.

Now I have to show him I'm *POOR*.

When I get off the bus, I head for the garage while Curtis stomps up the porch steps and into the house. Daddy is, of course, working and singing. But when he sees me, he looks so happy, and boy does *that* make showing him my spelling test that much harder.

It gets hard to swallow, and I'm already sweating when he says "Hi" and asks me about school.

I pull the paper out and explain everything. "Will you sign it, so I don't have to show Mother? She gets really angry with me when I show her my papers from school." I talk really fast, so I won't lose my nerve.

He takes the paper, "Dolly do you get a lot of papers with this word written on the top of them?" I nod and am happy when my curls bounce over my eyes, keeping me from seeing how he's looking at me.

"Dolly, how about you bring home the list of spelling words each week, and we can work on it out here? I will quiz you while I'm working, okay? It will be our secret." Daddy makes a *shhhh* sound with his finger to his lips.

"Oh, thank you, Daddy! You saved my life!" I say, jumping up and down.

He smiles. "Well, now, I wouldn't go that far."

"I would. You don't know how upset Mother gets with me about my bad grades."

He sighs. "I will sign your paper for you. Your Mother doesn't need to know. I'll leave the paper in your toolbox. Before you get on the bus tomorrow, come out to the garage, and get it." I run and hug him as tight as I can. "Thanks, Daddy. You're the best."

The next day at school, Mrs. Young asks for our signed papers. "Good Job, Sarah. I'm glad you brought this back on time. I am proud of you." "She is proud of me?" Mrs. Young stands by my desk and reads my daddy's signature. "I see you had your Dad sign the paper?" "Yes, he did. Mrs. Young." She stands at my desk, looking down at me for a few extra seconds before she walks away with my paper.

Then, Mrs. Young stands at the front of the room, pointing at the chalkboard. "Class, today is Elizabeth's birthday, so we have a special celebration planned."

Elizabeth is lucky; she gets to have a birthday. I've never had one in school or at home. None of my teachers have ever asked when mine is, and I never bring treats in like other kids do.

Daddy had told me I was almost nine, so I must have had close to *nine* birthdays. I will have to ask him about that.

Elizabeth's mom, Mrs. Brenda, brings in cupcakes covered in fluffy white stuff and sprinkles. Mrs. Brenda walks around the room handing out one to each of us. I love cupcakes. The last time I had one was at a school birthday party last year.

I take a bite.

Another girl in class, Millie Frank, says, "You don't eat your cupcake 'til we sing 'Happy Birthday, dummy!'"

"Millie, we don't call other students names in this class. Remember our class rules," Mrs. Young reminds her.

Soon after Millie gets scolded, Mrs. Young puts a crown on Elizabeth's head, and everyone sings and cheers for her birthday. Well, everyone except Millie, who is sitting off by herself with her lip puffed out and a scowl on her face, and me. I am quiet, so no one looks this way and notices that I've started to eat my cupcake.

After singing and blowing out the candles, everyone races back to their seats to gobble down their cupcakes. Slowly, I eat the rest of mine. When we're finished, Mrs. Young says, "Okay, class, let's give Elizabeth the cards and presents you have for her."

Millie Frank is over getting in trouble now and is the first one up to Elizabeth's desk. "Here, Elizabeth, I got you a card *and* a present. Open the envelope with the card first and then open my present." She bosses Elizabeth around like she does to everyone.

Elizabeth does as she's told. When she opens the envelope, she reads the card aloud. Elizabeth tears the pretty paper off and pulls out a toy.

I can't believe she *ripped up* that beautiful paper because I would keep it. I'd put it in my plastic dresser drawers or use it to make cards. But I have no pretty paper to make cards, so I stay in my seat. I don't have anything to give to Elizabeth.

While she is opening all the presents, the teacher walks up to me slowly, acting like I'm a dog that might bite her. "Sarah, why are you sitting back here and not up with the other students?"

"I don't know." I shrug. "Where did they get the money to buy her presents?"

"I'm not sure. Maybe their parents help them shop for presents," Mrs. Young bends down on one knee to be even with my desk.

"My mother would never give me money for anything." I exhale.

88

"What, exactly, is a birthday? I know some kids have them, but I don't know how to get one."

Mrs. Young stares at me for a few seconds before she reaches up and moves my hair away from my face. "Everyone has a birthday, Sarah."

"Not me and my brother Curtis." The words barely come out of my mouth.

Tears start rolling down Mrs. Young's cheeks.

Oh no. Now I've upset the one person who's nice to me at school. "I'm sorry, Mrs. Young."

She reaches over the desk, but I don't want her to touch me. I yank my hand back.

Mrs. Young tips her head to one side. "Well, Sarah, do you know what day you were born?"

"I don't know what you mean," I whisper. "Daddy said I am almost nine, but that's all I know."

She puts her hand over her mouth, and more tears run down her cheeks. "Sarah, would you like to have a birthday at school?" "I sure would, Mrs. Young!" I say happily.

She wipes her tears away, claps her hands, and smiles, making me think she is glad I'm getting a birthday. I clap too, and Mrs. Young says,

"I am glad you are excited, Sarah!"

"Does excited mean happy, Mrs. Young?"

"Why, yes, it does."

"Then I'm very excited," I say, sitting up straight in my seat.

After Elizabeth's finished, Mrs. Young has everyone gather around for an announcement. "Class, tomorrow is Sarah's birthday. We'll make cards later today, and, you can bring in a present for her tomorrow." Then, Mrs. Young writes *September 19—Sarah Bailey* on the blackboard.

I can hardly wait for the day to end and tomorrow to get here. I hope Mother knows how to make cupcakes and bring them to the school for me like Elizabeth's mom. I wonder how she'll carry my birthday treats *and* Emma into the school. Maybe Mother will leave Emma with my sister Christy and bring the cupcakes in by herself. Or perhaps she'll put Emma in a stroller and push her in with one hand while carrying the box full of cupcakes in the other. I can't wait to go home and tell Daddy that it will be my birthday tomorrow at school.

But when I get off the bus, Mother's waiting. "Don't bother your father. He's workin' on a big job."

Darn, she just *has* to ruin my excitement.

And then, I don't even get to tell Daddy about my birthday at dinner because he doesn't come in from the garage to eat with us. And I can't tell him at bedtime either because I fall asleep before he walks through our room.

But that's okay because I'm so excited about my birthday tomorrow. I can tell him all about it later.

The following day, I look all around for the cupcakes but don't see any. Mother doesn't mention anything about my birthday. I want to ask her, but I don't want her to put my hands under the water. The last time she did that, I got these swishy, watery bumps on them, and when those suckers busted open, it felt like a bunch of bees stinging me all at the same time.

What am I going to do when the kids in my class make fun of me for not having cupcakes? I have to figure it out before I get to school. Maybe I should get off at the next stop, walk to the sluice pipe, and hide there all day.

I glance out the window. Nope, that won't work 'cause I'm already too far away.

I *could* go to the school nurse and tell her I'm sick...

Or I can tell everyone that Mother has a cold and couldn't make them, and then maybe, by tomorrow, they'll forget all about it.

Oh, why did I agree to have a birthday in the first place? How could I ever think Mother would make cupcakes and bring them to school for me? She is nothing like Elizabeth's Mother, Mrs. Brenda, who brought cupcakes, and hugged and kissed her in front of everyone at school. Mother doesn't even do that to me at home.

I walk into the classroom, ready to tell everyone that Mother was too sick to bake when Mrs. Young calls me up to her desk and opens a container. She leans down as I stand in front of her and whispers, "I made vanilla and chocolate. I hope that's okay."

Yay! I'll have cupcakes! Yay! The kids won't know Mother is a mean witch. Yay! I wish Mrs. Young was my mom.

Everyone sings *Happy Birthday* to me. And *this* time, I wait to eat my cupcake because I won't make the same mistake twice.

I get a lot of pretty cards, not reading them out loud since that's too hard, but I say, "Thank you" after opening each one. The few toys I get are small enough to keep in my desk at school, making me happy. I don't think taking them home is a good idea because, at home, I don't have any toys. If Mother found them, she'd ask where I got them, and I would get in trouble. Plus, Curtis would find out I got them for my birthday, and he might be sad because he didn't get to have a birthday too.

"Yup, I'm definitely going to leave them here. I have plenty of room in my desk now since we cleaned them out yesterday.

My birthday is now my favorite holiday. The rest of the class always seems more excited about Santa Claus and Christmas than their birthdays. In December each year, my teachers have us read books about Santa. They've also had us write lists of what we want from him.

I write a letter every year, and, every year, the other kids come back from Christmas talking about all the toys they got left for them under a tree and in their stockings. Many of them are happy because they got the presents they told Santa they wanted in their letter. Last year I spent every day we had off for Christmas break running around outside looking under every tree for the minnow net I asked for in my letter to Santa.

I never got it.

Afterward, I asked Daddy why we don't celebrate holidays at our house, "That's a fair question, Dolly, and you have the right to know why, but it's a long story that I'll explain to you when you're older." But I want to know now. I'm tired of being different.

Today, I was just like all the other kids. I had a birthday thanks to Mrs. Young.

Why did Mrs. Young give me a birthday instead of my own Mother?
I plan to find out why.

Chapter 13
Daddy's Shirt & Don't Leave

*I cry with everything I have left in me, all the pain in me
pushing out through the tears that stain Daddy's shirt.*

Yawning, I drag myself into the kitchen behind a coughing Curtis, who
kept me up all night. I was looking forward to the weekend and playing
outside today, but I'm exhausted.

"Curtis, are ya sick?" Mother spins around from the kitchen counter.
"Don't go sneezin' and coughin' all over my kitchen. You'll get the rest
of us sick. Cover your nose and mouth. Geez. Ya look sick, boy. Lemme
take your temperature." She marches Curtis to the bathroom with her.

If Mother is taking Curtis to the bathroom, I will follow her, making
sure she doesn't put his hands under the hot water. While she's never
done that to Curtis and never gets as upset at him as she does with me, I
need to make sure she doesn't start now.

Thankfully, I don't hear any water running as I stand by our beds
listening.

"Well, boy, ya have a fever, so you're stuck stayin' in bed today. Do
ya want to eat or go back to bed now?"

"Bed."

I go back to the kitchen as Curtis flops on his bed 'cause I don't
want Mother to catch me listening in on them. I make it to the table before
Mother gets back to the kitchen.

"You're on your own today." She doesn't even look at me. "Your
brother's sick. Eat your breakfast and head outside."

I woof down my food, and though I still want another slice of toast,
I don't bother asking because she'll just say no, like always.

I tiptoe through our room to get dressed, though I'm not sure why

I'm being quiet. Not only does Curtis not wake up easily, but today, since he's sick, he's snoring more loudly than ever.

I hurry to get outside. Mother doesn't have to tell me more than once, "to git outta here." Anything to get away from her. I stop at the bottom of the porch and look up at all the clouds, remembering how Daddy taught me to tell time by checking where the sun is in the sky. We can usually hear Mother calling us, but other times, the sky can tell me.

When the sun is directly over top of me—Lunch. Today this will not be easy to do because of all the clouds. So instead, I'll make sure to listen for Mother.

Today is kinda boring without Curtis at the creek with me. Maybe I should practice catching minnows to beat him in our next contest. I get the cup out from under the L-shaped rock and chase the tiny fish in the water. Curtis makes it look easy, and he does it without falling in. I can't say the same thing for myself. The water is getting colder now that it's September, so I'm careful not to fall on my butt and get wet. I've been here for a while now, so I tilt my head toward the sky and find the sun behind the clouds. It isn't right above me, so I keep practicing.

Just when I catch a minnow, I hear a noise. Someone's coming through the pricker bushes toward the creek.

Who could it be? It's not Curtis; he's home, sick. It can't be Johnny and Joanie either—they're not gonna come back after we kicked their butts. Who else could it be?

What if…

What if it's *Derek*? I'm all alone.

I should run and hide, do something before whoever it is finds me and does…

The pipe! I'll get in there—

"Dolly?"

"*Daddy?*" What's he doing here?

Oh no!

Did something happen to Curtis? He is really sick today. Something terrible must've happened for Daddy to walk down the road and through our pricker bush path.

"Dolly, Mother's been calling for you. Why don't you make your way up the stream to the garage, so you don't get yourself in trouble?"

Uh, oh. My heart's thumping in my chest. If Daddy came all the way here to tell me Mother was looking for me, she must've been calling for a very long time. If Mother has to call or speak to us more than once, the second time usually comes with a face slap, hands under hot water, a flyswatter to the back of my legs, or a spanking—all of which really hurts.

"I'm coming," is all I can choke out.

He walks away. I empty my cups and then start stepping from one rock to another until I reach the bank path that leads me to the side of the garage. After climbing the muddy creek bank, I stop quickly when I hear Mother's voice.

"Where is she? Have you seen her today? I've been callin' her nonstop for the past twenty minutes."

"Check the mud pie station behind the house. Sarah was there a little while ago using the scrap metal to make a pretend oven." Daddy points to the back of the house.

She takes a deep breath and blows it out, which she always does when she's about to start yelling. "Ya let her play with metal from the damn cars in the backyard?" Mother sounds more like she's scolding Daddy rather than wanting an answer. "I know they give us insurance for her, but I don't need to spend my time runnin' her to the emergency room."

I don't hear Daddy answer, but I hear the stones crunching as Mother walks away from the garage. I don't know what insurance means or why she gets some for me, but I don't have time to worry about that. I need to move my butt, or else I *will* get caught.

Then it hits me: Daddy is trying to save me from Mother. Instead of hollering for me to come home—because Mother would have heard him—he walked down to tell me. Then, he gives me the chance to get onto the driveway before Mother can realize I'm not out back making a pretend oven.

I run fast around the left side of the garage, stopping quickly in the driveway to catch my breath. Daddy stands there, winking as I run past before he goes back to work.

Mother finds me.

Her face changes from *huffy* to *mad* in just a couple of seconds. Mother makes sure Daddy isn't watching before grabbing my arm and dragging me toward the house. She pinches my arm so tight it burns.

"Mother, you're walking too fast."

She ignores me, and I fall to my knees twice. Then, instead of helping me up, she yanks my arm harder, dragging me 'til I get myself on my feet. I stumble a couple more times, losing my balance, but I somehow stay up.

"When I call your name, young lady, that means ya get your ass inside this house. Got it?"

I will *not* cry even though my arm feels like it's on fire. "Yes, Mother."

She pulls me up the steps and into the living room, where she finally let's go. My arm's all red and turning purple already in some places. After that, it'll probably turn black and blue like so many spots on my body from Mother's punishments and my older brothers' games.

"It's lunch, and you're damn lucky I'm even feedin' ya today after makin' me waste all that time lookin' for ya!"

Mother stomps over to where I am standing in the living room and grabs my already sore arm. I try to duck around her when I see her coming, but I can't get away fast enough. She pulls me quickly into the kitchen. She yanks a chair out from the table and puts it behind me.

Bam!

Mother puts her hand on my chest and pushes me backward. I fall into the hard kitchen chair.

"Sit down and don't ya dare move," she yells while throwing a peanut butter and jelly sandwich at me.

"Hurry up and eat so ya can git out of my hair. Ya can stay out for the rest of the day."

Peanut butter and jelly makes the pain in my arm better. I take a bite. Mmmm. Just as I bring the sandwich back up to my mouth, Mother shrieks pointing at the floor.

"Sarah! Ya, didn't wipe off your feet again! Look at the mud ya tracked in here."

Before I know it, I'm being yanked again by Mother. She grabs the same sore arm and pulls me out of the chair. My sandwich falls out of my hands and drops to the floor.

I will not cry. I will not cry. No matter how much my arm hurts or how much Mother scares me. "Do you want me or your father to spank ya this time?"

"Daddy." My voice is soft, but that's because I actually have hope for once. Daddy won't run my hands under the water, and he won't spank me very hard. He never does.

Mother drags me to the garage. "Joseph!"

Daddy's legs are sticking out from underneath a car. He has Elvis music playing on the radio and is humming along to it.

Mother turns it off. "Joseph!"

Daddy rolls out from under the car and glances between Mother and me.

He frowns.

Mother releases my arm and places her hands on her hips. "She's done it again. There's mud all over the livin' room and kitchen floor from her filthy feet. Your shoebox hasn't worked. I want her spanked."

Daddy had made me a box on the front porch to put my shoes in. But since I'm not wearing shoes, it wouldn't have worked even if Mother hadn't dragged me into the house.

He pushes his safety goggles to the top of his head and sighs. "Donna, does she really need a spanking? Can't you just make her clean it up? She likes to help out."

Mother twists her mouth. "No! After makin' me look all over for her today, and then this stunt? I have had it with her! So, you do it, or *I will*."

Daddy sighs again, but he stands up, takes off his gloves, then sits on his stool.

Daddy waves me over, then looks at the cracked cement floor.

I do, too, as I walk to him.

He takes my hand. "Lie down across my knee, Sarah." Then I see him look at my arm—the one Mother used to drag me. His eyes get big, and something passes over them like a storm cloud. Daddy raises my arm so he can see where Mother grabbed me.

He stays quiet as I lie down over his knee, then spanks me twice.

They hurt, but they're nothing compared to Mother hitting me with her hand or the flyswatter. The metal handle of that flyswatter stings like crazy on the back of my legs. I lose count of how many times she hits me with it.

"Really, Joseph, that's all you're doin'? Hit her again." Mother crosses her arms. "Your love taps didn't even hurt her." She makes a disgusted noise. "Just forget it. Next time, I'll do it myself." She turns around fast and storms out of the garage, leaving Daddy and me alone.

I squeeze my eyes shut tight. The thought of Mother spanking me next time makes my stomach do cartwheels. Then it grumbles, and I realize I'm also hungry. Mother was too mad to let me finish my sandwich.

Daddy helps me up, and my tears begin to fall now that Mother has left. He frowns again and pulls me into a hug.

I cry with everything I have left in me, all the pain in me pushing out through the tears that stain Daddy's shirt.

He pats my back. The smell of his Old Spice makes me want to tell him everything. But instead, I just cry because talking to him about the games the boys play with us could make things worse for Curtis and me. "I'm so sorry, Dolly. Please don't drag mud into the house anymore. Okay?"

I nod and hang on to the only grown-up who loves me.

Then Daddy pulls out the dollar he always gives me after the spankings. "Go to the store and get yourself some ice cream, honey. That'll make it all better." His idea of making the spanking and the tears go away is to let me go for a long bike ride to get a mint chocolate chip ice cream cone. "I fixed the chain on your bike, so it should be all good to go." He points to my bike, which he'd made this past summer by welding parts of other bikes together. "Be careful riding to the ice cream shop."

"I will, Daddy."

Ice cream is another of my favorite things, but I'd give it up any day if the spankings would only stop. I don't do what I do wrong on purpose, but that never matters. I used to say I was sorry— and I was— but that didn't help either. At least, not with Mother. I still tell Daddy I'm sorry after I make a mistake.

By the time I get back from the ice cream store, it is late in the day, and supper is ready. "Hey, Dolly, back in time for dinner. How was your bike ride?" "My legs are killing me," I tell him as I wobble, walking my bike back into the garage. "That is a long ride. I bet your legs are tired. Let's get in the house and eat dinner. Get the lights, Dolly, and let's close the garage down."

No one talks much at supper. Derek isn't there, and Vinnie and

Terry are out with friends. Curtis never speaks, but Mother and Daddy hardly say a word to one another. Something seems very wrong.

After I go to bed, I hear Daddy and Mother arguing.

"Don't make excuses, Donna. That child had a bruise on her arm, and I know you put it there. It's not the first time I've seen marks on her. We've discussed this before."

"But Jos—"

"No excuses. If it happens again, I'm leaving you!"

I've never heard Daddy this mad. If he leaves Mother, I'm left alone here with everyone else. I feel sick. Thank goodness I didn't tell him about Mother, Vinnie, Terry, and especially Derek. He'll never see my bruises again.

Never.

This morning, Curtis is still not feeling well enough to go outside and play. His temperature is around 100, and he's coughing even more than yesterday. So, Mother gives Curtis dry toast, water, and some cough medicine.

"Yuck, this medicine is gross." Some of the red syrup runs down his chin.

"Ya want to feel better, right? If we can get ya feelin' better, ya can go play with your sister rather than bein' in bed. So, I need ya to take this medicine. Let's try it again." She puts more red stuff on the spoon.

Curtis doesn't spit any of it out, though he does make a gagging sound like he's going to throw up.

"Now go back to bed and lie down. This should help ya feel better soon," Mother says in a sweet voice.

Why doesn't she talk like that to me? What do I do that makes her hate me so much? I feel sad sitting at the table eating my cereal like I could… Why would I want to cry over Mother? She's always been mean to me. But, for the first time, my heart hurts just as much as my hands do after scalding water.

Thank goodness I get to go to Sunday school today. I'm almost at the door when Mother grabs me and drags me into the bathroom.

"Well, young lady, it looks like this is going to be the best way to punish ya so ya can't show your father your bruises. Let's see whatcha think about that." She turns on the hot water. "You're an ungrateful brat who's tryin' to ruin my marriage."

"Mother, I didn't show Daddy my bruises. I swear. Mother, please don't hurt me again." She acted like she didn't hear me while she shoved both my hands under the hot water.

I try to think about other things when she is hurting me, so I won't cry in front of her, like helping Daddy shave in this bathroom.

He sits me on top of the sink and hands me his razor after running it over his skin. Then I hit it on the sink. And finally, he tells me to run it under the water for him before giving it back. He never says, "Hurry up, Dolly," even when I know I'm taking longer than he would need to do it himself.

Once I saw blood running down his cheek onto his neck. I'd gotten really scared. "You're bleeding, Daddy!"

"Don't worry, Dolly. I'm okay. It's just a little cut." He'd handed me a white, pencil-looking thing and told me to rub it on his cut. "This will stop the bleeding."

At first, I thought Daddy was silly because a pencil is for writing and erasing mistakes, not for cuts. But it worked because the bleeding stopped.

This memory is one of my happy times in this bathroom that I hate, and I want to be here with Daddy instead of Mother and my burning hands.

Hiding my bruises is going to be super important. He can never see them again. I'll do whatever it takes to make sure Daddy never leaves.

Daddy can never leave me.

Chapter 14
Sorry Worms & Inside with Mother

"Sorry, worms," I drop the cup and I take off,
running as fast as I can toward the garage.
The engine screams behind me. The boys are chasing me. I thought they
might keep going past me, but they stopped near our driveway.
I have nowhere else to go, so I run to the edge of the driveway.
One of the boys opens the car door.
He reaches out to grab me, but then he sees Daddy
at the same time I do.

The mirror is all steamed, and the water is shut off.

My hands?

Are sore and red when Mother yells in my face.

"Git outside and outta my sight. I don't want to see ya 'til lunch time, ya hear?"

Thank goodness I have church today.

I run fast as I can to the garage, making sure to tuck my hands into my pants pocket so Daddy won't see them.

"Hey Dolly, are you ready for church?" He smiles with his usual big smile.

"Yes, I am."

The blue bus arrives right on time, and we make our trip to the church, which I still like to call a math building. Once inside, I look for Debbie and Jackie. Debbie is sitting with her family one row behind me and waves. I then look for Jackie but don't see her anywhere.

"Child are you having a hard time sitting still this morning?" Miss Sandy asks me while patting my dirty knee. "Yes, I can't wait for Sunday school." "You can go back in just a few minutes. You won't have to sit here too much longer."

We sing church songs—All the kids walk to the front, and then Pastor Scott prays over us. "God, bless these children and help them learn all they can in Sunday school this morning, Amen." Jackie joins us upfront, saying, "We got behind a train on the way here."

"What's our teacher's name?" I ask Debbie and Jackie.

"We don't know. Our regular Sunday school teacher is Mrs. Krandle."

"So, who's here this week?" I need to know.

"We're not sure," Jackie answers. "Mrs. Krandle was sick last week. I don't know if the other teacher will ever come back." Jackie says it like it's no big deal.

But it *is* a big deal. It's a big deal to me because I didn't get to know the teacher's name, who was so kind and showed me how to pray to Jesus.

I'm so bummed out by this news. "How often has she been here when Mrs. Krandle's absent?"

"Just last Sunday," Debbie says.

Once? That means I may never see her again. *Oh, no!* Why didn't I thank her last week?

I'm still hoping Jackie's wrong, and we'll see her standing there when we walk into the classroom. But when we turn the corner, there stands… a new teacher—who I can only guess is Mrs. Krandle. I'm sad that my first Sunday school teacher is not here, but I'm still happy being at God's house.

We read the Bible. Mrs. Krandle calls it scriptures. She has me read a very short part with smaller words, and no one makes fun of me. When I finish, I wait for the laughing to start. "Jason, could you read the next few scriptures for us please." Jason starts reading.

No one is laughing at me. No one is laughing. I can't believe it. The other kids finish reading their parts. Jason finishes the reading, and we spend the rest of class talking about Jesus and other people in the Bible. Mrs. Krandle reads us a story about Noah's Ark. *Holy Cow.* I never thought about all the animals that must be in the world 'til now. They all got on Noah's boat two by two. That boat had to be huge, like this church.

Then we make this awesome bookmark with a scripture and a picture of Jesus with a lamb. We color and put stickers and glitter all over it. Of course, I use too much, so mine takes forever to dry.

"Don't worry, Sarah," Mrs. Krandle reassures me. "If your picture isn't ready to go by time you leave, you can pick it up next week."

I hope it dries fast today because I want to take it to school with me and use it in my library book on horses.

Jackie and Debbie do a great job on their bookmarks though Debbie uses too much glitter like me. Mrs. Krandle has us lay them side by side on the window ledge to dry. "Are you sure no one will take my bookmark?" I ask Mrs. Krandle over and over again, but she answers me nicely every time. "Yes, Sarah, I can tell you are worried about it. But I promise you, no one will take your bookmark."

I like Mrs. Krandle, but I miss the teacher from last week, who taught me to pray and sing to Jesus. Maybe I'll see her again someday.

The blue bus drops me off in front of my house, and, after lunch, I stop in the garage where Daddy is cleaning and doing bills. "Hey Daddy, I'm going to head to the creek and look for worms." Most days, I have to dig for them, but sometimes they're just lying on the ground squirming around when it rains like it has today.

"Did you know fisherman use nightcrawlers to catch fish?"

"No, I didn't know that." The only fish I know how to catch are minnows in a cup.

"Fish like worms, so when you put them on the end of a hook and throw the line in the water, fish will bite and then… *Shazam* you have a fish." Daddy pretends like he is fishing while telling me how to do it.

"Do you have any hooks and lines Daddy?"

"No honey. I don't have the time or patience to fish."

Daddy pauses, looking lost in thought. "Maybe we should sell nightcrawlers. We could put a stand at the end of the driveway and put a little cooler in it. We could keep the worms in the garage fridge, and then you could load up your cooler and take them out to the stand."

"Ooh, yuck, Daddy. Why would you put worms in the fridge with your drinks?" I squinch up my face at him.

"Because it keeps them alive longer."

I keep the same look on my face. Worms in a fridge grosses me out.

Daddy laughs. "It *would* be kinda gross to keep worms with my beer. I got an idea. Why don't you go out back and dig out the old fridge in the junk pile behind the garage?

"Will it even work if it's out in the junk pile?" "Well, we won't know unless we try, now, will we?" He shrugs and puts his hands up. "If it still works, we can use it by the road for self-service."

"What is self-service?"

"It's where people can just drive up, put their money in the can, open the fridge door, take a cup of worms, and drive off. This way, people won't bother me for the worms while I'm working."

I go through the junk pile, and I find the fridge.

I make the mistake of looking inside. *Whoa.* No wonder Daddy wants to use this fridge. It already has dirt inside it for the worms, like the black, fuzzy stuff around our tub. I can put more mud pie dirt in it, so I won't even need cups. The worms can just crawl around.

I go back inside the garage. "I found the worm fridge." All I can think about is how cool it will be to sell worms. "When can we start?"

"Hold on, hold on. Give me a few weeks and I'll get the stand built for you."

"Okay, good deal." I give him an okay sign with my fingers.

He laughs and goes back to work.

I head to the creek to collect the nightcrawlers. I was right; they are everywhere. I'm going to make a lot of money tomorrow on these suckers.

Daddy will be so excited to see all these worms I caught. The worms are trying to crawl out, so I cover the top with the bottom of my shirt. I would skip down this road if I wasn't holding them. Once I show Daddy how many I got, I'm sure he'll want to get that stand built right away.

I hear it before I see it—a car coming up the road behind me. Then, as the engine gets louder, I turn around just as they drive past.

Splash! They hit a puddle of water.

I am soaked.

There are a lot of boys in the car and one of them screams out the window, "Want to go for a ride, little girl?

Do they know me? I wonder as they drive by.

Then I see their blue car turn around in Mr. Bob's driveway. Now they're coming toward me and pulling over on the other side of the road.

They must be lost. So, I begin to walk across the road toward the car.

"What do you have under your shirt?" I don't know these boys, but maybe they want to buy some of my worms to take fishing.

Before I can answer, another boy yells, "She's got tits in there." And they all laugh.

I stop instantly in the middle of the road.

I've never heard of anyone calling worms tits before. Daddy calls them nightcrawlers but never tits.

Then another boy says he likes my stomach and looks at me like Derek does.

Suddenly, I'm scared.

"Hey, wanna go for a ride and... play." *Play what?*

"Yeah," another boy shouts. "Hey, little girl, wanna play doctor and patient?"

That's the game Derek plays with me—these boys do *not* want to buy worms.

The garage is so close now. If I run, I can make it before the car can turn around. The only problem is that I'm not going to make it while holding the worms.

"Sorry, worms," I drop the cup and take off, running as fast as I can toward the garage.

The engine screams behind me. The boys are chasing me. I thought they might keep going past me, but they stop near our house.

Just as I hit the edge of the driveway, one of the boys opens the car door. He reaches out to grab me, but Daddy sees it happening at the exact moment.

"Hey!" he yells.

The rest of the boys scream, "Go! Go!"

The boy trying to grab me falls back in the car when the driver steps on the gas to take off.

I keep running and then leap into Daddy's arms.

"What happened, Dolly?"

"The boys asked me to play doctor, so I got scared and ran. Then I had to drop the worms and Curtis's cup because they started chasing me." Suddenly in the middle of my story, I can't breathe. "Take it easy and catch your breath," he says while rubbing my back.

"I want you to get inside the house and lock the door, honey." I head toward the house, then stop on the steps.

Daddy walks out of the garage with his gun, hops into his truck, and drives off in the same direction as the boys.

Mother likes to make fun of him for driving like an old man because he goes so slow. But, today, Daddy pulls out of the driveway so fast that the rocks kick up and ping against his truck. I run into the living room, lock the front door, then run past Mother, Curtis, and Emma.

Mother throws down a magazine and stands up. "Now where the hell is your father goin' in such a hurry? He has work to do! What the hell did ya do, Sarah?"

Without stopping or answering her, I run to my room and climb into the bed. In my head, I keep singing, *Jesus loves me, this I know, for the Bible tells me so* until I hear Daddy's truck pull back into the driveway.

"It's about damn time." I hear Mother say in her grumpy voice.

The front lock clicks. "Where the hell did ya go and why do ya have your gun? Did Sarah get herself in trouble?"

Daddy doesn't answer Mother, but I can hear his footsteps coming up onto the porch, and he shouts, "Dolly, Dolly!

After getting down from my bunk and running into the living room, I see Daddy put his gun on the coffee table and opens his arms to hug me.

Mother just scowls at us.

"Did you catch them, Daddy?"

He shook his head. "I chased them up Benton Hill and around City Park, but I couldn't catch them. I'm pretty sure I scared them off, though. I don't think they'll show their faces 'round here again anytime soon."

Mother makes an unhappy noise. "Was that really necessary? What happened, anyway?"

Daddy narrows his eyes at Mother. "I'll tell you about it later." She doesn't say another word.

"I'm so upset I had to throw my worms to the ground. If you saw how many I caught, you'd want to make that stand for me right away."

"Sarah, your father, is too bu—" Mother begins, but Daddy looks at her the way he did just moments ago, and she doesn't even finish the last word.

He kisses the top of my head. "It's okay, Dolly. I'm sure you will be able to find plenty more to sell."

Daddy looks at Mother. "I need you to keep her inside for the rest of the day." He sounds angry. "She'll be back in school tomorrow. Not much left of the day anyway, so a few hours indoors to keep her safe shouldn't be a problem."

Mother doesn't answer. She just wrinkles up her face at him, and he locks eyes with her, glaring right back. "I suppose not," she finally answers, still scowling at Daddy.

Daddy pats the top of my head, picks up his gun, then goes back out to the garage.

As soon as he's off the porch steps, Mother points at the floor.

In my rush to get inside the house quickly, I didn't clean off my bare feet again. It's probably all over my bed, but Mother won't mind it there.

She comes over, grabs my arm, pulls down my pants, and spanks me hard many times. Today, I don't get a choice.

When she finishes, she says, "Go get the Pine-Sol, some rags, and the bucket in the laundry room and clean up this mess. And, while you're at it, scrub the kitchen floor, too. You've nuthin' else better to do today since your father thinks ya should stay in. This will keep ya busy."

I have to walk by my brothers' bedroom to get the supplies. Derek's room stinks like the rotten fish we find down by the creek. It makes me grind my teeth together.

Mother doesn't care what those boys in the car tried to do to me today, and she's really not happy about keeping me inside so I stay safe.

I'm not either. I mean, how can staying in the house keep me safe? I have a better chance of getting away from those boys than I do from Mother.

When I get back into the living room, I ask Mother, "Why do I have to clean the kitchen floor if I didn't mess it up?" *Smack!*

The Pine-Sol drops to the floor, hitting Mother's foot after she hits my face.

She cries out, "Pick up that damn Pine-Sol and get the floors done, ya pain in my ass! The next time you are mouthy with me, we'll take a little walk to the sink after I fill your mouth with dish soap." I sigh and start my chores.

"I've finished the entrance and kitchen," I tell Mother. She sits on the couch eating her adult snack, potato chips, and watching soap operas. "Now get the vacuum cleaner and sweep the carpet in the living room and my bedroom. Don't just sweep where ya tracked the mud, neither. Sweep it all. Make it fast, too. I got a show I want to watch." She says all this while crunching on her chips.

I plug in the sweeper and push it across the carpet. It's heavy, and I hit the leg of the coffee table with it. "If ya hit that coffee table leg one more time, I'll spank your ass again," Mother says, almost grinning at me.

She doesn't care how heavy it is; she just likes the idea of punishing me.

Mother points to a spot on the rug by the boots when I finish the carpet. "Ya missed a spot. As a matter of fact, why don't ya clean up all these spots on the rug?"

Do it yourself! I wish I could yell at her, but I don't dare. My hands still hurt from this morning before church. Plus, I got spanked by Daddy yesterday and Mother already today. That's enough punishment.

I don't know how much longer I can stand being inside this house with Mother.

"Sarah" after making mud pies.

"Sarah" and "Curtis"

Derek's Buckle

Mama Cat

Math Building

Dr. Sharon Zaffarese-Dippold
Melissa Mulhollan

Sluice Pipe Fort

Chapter 15
Because of You & A Runny Nose

The car door closes behind me, and all of Mother's niceness is gone
"What's wrong with ya, Sarah?
Ya can't even stay in school?" she yells.
Emma opens her mouth and starts crying loudly. "Great.
Now, look what ya did! My baby is cryin' because of you!

Daddy has done it.

There is my worm stand by the weeping willow tree next to the driveway. It's bright yellow, with a sign that reads, *Dolly's Nightcrawlers, $.25 a cup* in black letters. The colors remind me of a bumblebee.

I drop my books and sprint toward the garage. "I love it, Daddy! Thank you!" I leap into his arms.

He swings me around. "I'm glad you like it, Dolly. Come with me so I can show you how it works." He points to the orange extension cords that run from the stand to inside the garage. "People can pull up, grab their own worms, and put their money in the can." He glued the can on top of the stand using special glue from the garage. He also glued the coffee can lid down so no one could open it but put a hole with a black plug in the bottom of the can.

Daddy gets down on the ground and shows me how it works.

"See, Dolly? No one can take your money because they won't be able see this black plug if they don't know it's there. And the stand is too heavy to move with the fridge in it." He's as happy about making this stand for me as I am to get it.

"Always make sure you put the plug in after you remove it. You can keep all the money in the other coffee can in the garage by your toolbox so no one can get to it."

"What if someone takes a cup and worms and doesn't put money in the can?"

"Well, Dolly, some people might take them, but I only want you to think about the people who will be honest and pay. I like to believe people are more honest than not."

"Do you know that if you use a flashlight in our yard after dark, you can catch a lot of nightcrawlers? I think you'll catch more here than by the creek." He hands me a big flashlight. "The only time you can look for nightcrawlers in the dark is in our yard. Deal?"

"Deal."

The flashlight will be kept in the metal fort by the garage so no one will find it. I can use it even when Daddy is out with Mother and the garage door is locked.

"Can I play in my worm stand now?"

"Of course. Do you like the color I used on it?"

"Yellow is perfect. That way, people will see it from the road."

Daddy nods, and I follow him into the garage to get the cups for the worms.

When I open the fridge, I see it's all cleaned up and looks brand new.

The next few hours I spend playing at my stand. Not many cars go by on our road, but whenever I hear one coming, I hide by the closest junk metal car until I'm sure they're not going to stop.

Out of nowhere, it begins to rain and thunder. Now I know I'll have to go inside the house soon. Mother lets me stay outside when it's raining, but not when there is thunder and lightning. This isn't Mother's rule because she could care less. Daddy made it up a long time ago.

"Sarah, git inside this house right now! It's lightnin' out there, and supper is ready!"

I go inside and change my clothes, but my hair's still dripping wet at dinner. Daddy looks at me, "Donna, do you think you could get Dolly a haircut or trim her bangs a little? I can't see her beautiful eyes with her hair hanging down over them."

"No, thank you," I say almost before he's finished talking. As much as I hate having hair in my eyes, I hate being teased for having a unibrow even more.

After supper, I am freezing, so I get a bath to warm myself up. Then, when I'm done, I stand in front of the living room window, trying to see my worm stand in the dark and through the rain before Mother shoos me off to bed.

Goodnight worm stand.

The next day, my body hurts all over, and my nose has this yellow snot coming out of it. At breakfast, I tell Mother, "I don't feel good, and my body hurts." "Well, ya ain't stayin' home from school today, so don't even try playin' sick. Git finishin' your breakfast so ya can catch the bus in time for school today." She was nice to Curtis when he was sick. Why is she so mean to me all the time? "Hey, Rudolph," Terry teases me. Mother says nothing to him as if she didn't hear him, but he is standing next to her at the kitchen sink. So, I know she can hear him picking on me.

Once I arrive at school, I put my head down on my desk to hide from everything. Mrs. Young notices right away, "Sarah, are you okay this morning?" My nose runs the whole time my head is down, so when I sit up, snot is everywhere. She gets me a tissue and sends me to the nurse, who takes my temperature and calls Mother to come get me.

As much as I don't like school, knowing that Mother is coming makes my body hurt worse. She's going to be angry.

The nurse hands me a blue blanket. "Here you go, Sarah." She wraps it around my shoulders. "Honey, why don't you lie down on the cot?" Wrapping the blanket tighter around me, I lie down with my head facing the door so I can see when Mother comes in, but I don't stop shaking.

The nurse walks over to me. "Sarah, you can call me Mrs. Holly. I have some pop for you to drink and a package of Saltines to eat. It might help your stomach feel better." "What is pop, Mrs. Holly?" "Haven't you had pop before, Sarah?" "I think so, but it was orange color. Mother has pop, but tells us to stay out of it because it's her special drink." "Well, try it and let me know what you think." I take a quick sip and start giggling. It tickles my throat.

A boy comes in, throwing up in a garbage can, and I almost do the same thing. I hate that gagging sound. I lie back on the cot, wanting to turn away from him, but then I'd have to have my back to the door. I'm not about to do that because I'll miss seeing Mother come in when she gets here.

Mrs. Holly tells the boy to go wait on the other cot and pulls the curtain closed while she calls his mom to pick him up. His mom shows up before mine does, even though he came into the nurse's office a long time after me.

Mrs. Holly walks to my cot, sitting down. "Sarah, how far is your house from the school?" "I pass one stop sign on the way here."

She frowns, and I wonder if I've said something wrong. She rechecks my forehead, and before she walks away, my stomach growls, so I ask, "Do you have any toast in here?"

"I don't have any toast, but I do have some peanut butter crackers. Would you like some of those?" Would I *like* that? *Peanut butter? On crackers?* I bob my head up and down so fast I feel dizzy.

Mrs. Holly walks over to her desk drawer and quickly returns, handing me a whole package.

Looking down at it in my hand, I ask, "How many can I have?" She stops so fast it was like she'd run into a wall.

"How *many* can you have, Sarah? My dear, there are only six crackers in the entire package. You can have all of them."

"What? Really, Mrs. Holly, I can have all of them?" Barely believing my eyes.

All of them…

"Thank you."

I sneeze, wiping it on my shirt sleeve. "No, Sarah!" Mrs. Holly hands me a tissue. "You use a tissue for that and then wash your hands. Here, blow your nose, dear."

"Mother says I use too much toilet paper to blow my nose, so I use my shirt."

Her brown eyes crinkle up.

I take my first bite.

Yum.

What do you think of them?" She pats my shoulder.

"They're great. I love anything with peanut butter. These are now my fourth favorite food. First is a slice of toast with lots of butter on it. The second is a peanut butter and jelly sandwich. The third is cereal." Mrs. Holly laughs and sounds a lot like Daddy.

She makes a phone call from her desk and quietly talks, so I can't hear what she's saying. And, well, also because I'm chomping on these fantastic crackers.

Mrs. Holly hangs up the phone and offers me a piece of paper and a pencil. "Would you like to draw?" I shrug.

"How about you draw a pretty picture for me?"

I stop chewing. Draw? Something pretty? *Oh, no.* Just when I have someone else at school being nice to me, I'll mess it up because I can't draw, especially not something pretty.

Just then, the phone rings. After Mrs. Holly gets off the phone, she comes over to my cot, "Sarah, it's time to go." She walks me to the office where Mother is waiting with Emma. Mother put on some lipstick and tried to look nice like she did when Mrs. A. came to the house. She's smiling and talking nice to the office ladies.

"Let's get you home, honey, so you can get all better."

I look behind me, trying to see who Mother is speaking to. The only person behind me Mrs. Holly and I don't think Mother plans to take her home.

I turn back around.

Mother's lips tighten just a bit—I've seen that look before, and I know exactly what it means.

I nod, doing what I've been told.

She grabs my hand and walks me out of the building with Emma on her hip.

The car door closes behind me, and all of Mother's niceness is gone. "What is wrong with ya, Sarah? Ya can't even stay in school?" she yells.

Emma opens her mouth and starts crying really loud.

"Great. *Now,* look what ya did! My baby is cryin' because of you!"

Emma cries the whole way home making my head hurt worse. Then, when Mother pulls into the driveway, I'm too sick and tired to move.

She gets Emma out of the car and goes into the house, leaving me sitting there and looking up at the gray sky.

Daddy opens the car door. "Dolly, honey, what're you doing sitting out here when you've got yourself a runny nose? Let's get you inside so you can get some rest."

"Don't forget to take your boots off before you go inside." He opens the door for me.

I walk straight to my room, take off my coat, drop it onto the floor, then crawl into my bed and fall fast asleep. Finally, I sleep without being afraid, and no one bothers me. That has to be a first.

"Hey, Dolly," Daddy's voice wakes me. "I just came in from the garage, and Mother heated me some of that chicken noodle soup from a can. Do you want to have some soup with me? It's mmm, mmm good!"

I'm not hungry, even after sleeping all day. Those crackers kept my belly full, but when he mentions food and the idea of sitting with just him and eating, I'm suddenly starving.

I sit up and say, "Yes!" but I start to sway.

"Whoa, honey. Take it slow. How about you climb onto my back, and I'll carry you into the kitchen?"

Sitting on the edge of my bed, I hold onto Daddy's neck, and he carries me to the kitchen on his back. As we pass through the living room, I see Mother. She squints at me, and her forehead has lines all over it. Her face is as red as her hair as she watches us.

He sits me in my chair at the table. The hot soup makes my nose run. Daddy pulls a blue and white cloth out of his back pocket. "Hey, sweetie, let me wipe your nose with my hanky." Daddy is gentle. "Now that's better." He slides it back into his pants pocket. "Make sure you wipe your nose softly, so it doesn't get all red and sore, okay, honey?"

As he's telling me how to do it, I slurp my soup. He laughs, and I laugh, too, as a noodle sneaks out of the corner of my mouth and plops back into the bowl, which makes us laugh even harder.

"You two, quiet down out there. I just put Emma to bed, and I'm leaving to go see Christy. Joseph, make sure you listen for her in case she wakes up." She grabs her car keys and leaves the house.

Alone with Daddy, I have the perfect opportunity to ask him about something bothering me. "Daddy, I had a birthday at school." Daddy raises both eyebrows. "You did, did you?" I nod and swallow hard.

"How did that come about, Dolly?"

I take a deep breath and then tell him how the kids celebrate their birthdays at school. Their moms bring in treats for everyone. I tell him about the "Happy Birthday" song, cards, and pretty, wrapped gifts with toys inside.

"There's this girl Elizabeth, and on her birthday, everyone gave her cards and gifts. I stayed at my desk because I didn't have anything to give her. Mrs. Young talked to me about it and asked if I knew when I was born. I told her that you told me I was almost nine, but I never have birthdays."

He sits at the table and says nothing before looking at me again, so I can go on. "Mrs. Young asked if I would like to have a birthday at school, and I said yes! So, she put my name on the board, brought in cupcakes, had the kids make me cards, and they sang "Happy Birthday" to me. It was so cool, Daddy!"

He's quiet for a little while after I stop talking.

Then, finally, he speaks. "Well, I think you have a really great teacher this year, Dolly. I'm happy you had a birthday at school, but let's not mention it to your Mother, okay?"

"Okay, Daddy. So, is this like the other holidays? You will tell me later why I don't have a birthday at home?"

He smiles, "Yes, honey, it's exactly like the reason we don't do holidays in our home."

"Okay. And I won't say anything to Mother." I hold my pinky out to Daddy so we can do our pinky swear. It makes him laugh as we lock them together and shake.

When I finish my soup, I get a warm bath and go back to bed. But, before I do, I kneel and talk to Jesus.

"Dear Jesus, thank you for the rain, the nice nurse, the peanut butter crackers, and time alone with Daddy to eat our soup. Please help me feel better. I hope you never get sick, Jesus, because it doesn't feel good. Amen."

I wake up the following day still a little stuffy. My body feels tired and hurts everywhere.

"Git up and git ready for school. Let's git movin'," Mother yells at us.

There are no more nurse's office visits for a runny nose, no more pop, and no more peanut butter crackers. And no more soup with Daddy.

Oh, well. It was fun while it lasted.

Chapter 16
I'm too Late & Why Can't I

By the time I have Curtis hidden, I take off running through the bathroom, our bedroom and stop in the living room looking for Derek. When the coast is clear, I take off for the kitchen and head toward the food closet. Ping. Derek appears from behind the front door. I'm too late.

You can hear everything in my nose hit my hand as I sneeze. "Gross, Sarah," Curtis mumbles. Mother has ignored me until the snot on my hand is about to get wiped on my sleeve. "Wipe your damn hand on your napkin and come to the bathroom with me."

Oh no! I had to sneeze! I couldn't help it! So now I'm getting punished for it?

It takes everything I have to drag myself from the table, feeling hot and dizzy. Walking in a straight line to the bathroom is not an easy thing for me right now, as I'm zig-zagging and bumping into walls. Mother waves the thermometer at me. "Open up." At least she's not putting my hands under the hot water.

I bet that would make my temperature go up. A couple of minutes later, she says, "Go back to bed, Sarah." I crawl into my bunk and don't go back to school for days...

"Git up, it's time to go to school," Mother yelled throughout our tiny house.

"You too Sarah. You're well enough to go back to school today. Ya can at least get your ass there one day this week. I've had enough of ya lyin' around this house sneezin' all over the place."

Just then, my pillow is swiped out from under my head, "Let's get going, Bucky, time to go to school," Terry sang as he hit me over the head with my pillow. It didn't hurt. It was just really annoying. I don't know why Mother wouldn't let me miss today, since it is the last day of the week.

"Welcome back to school, Sarah. Are you feeling better?" I nod. "Good, I'm glad to hear it. I think you are going to have fun today because we will be doing some activities for Halloween." She leans down close to my desk, whispering, "Do you have a costume, or do you want to go to the costume closet with us during recess?" I don't want to miss recess, but I need a costume, and I won't be getting one from home. "I would like to go to the closet, Mrs. Young." She nods as she walks to her desk and writes on a piece of paper.

After lunch, the other third-grade teacher takes our class and his class outside to the playground while Mrs. Young takes four of his students and six kids from our class to the nurse's office, where they keep all the costumes.

When we get there, I can't believe what I'm seeing. There are racks of costumes hanging up and some folded on a table. Mrs. Young comes to the table where I am looking through piles of costumes. "Do you want to be a princess, Sarah?" "No way," I say quickly. "All right. So, what would you like to be this year? Any ideas? "My daddy says I am an Indian."

"That doesn't surprise me. Many Native Americans have dark hair, dark eyes, and darker skin like you do." "I'd like to find an Indian costume." We call them Native Americans, not Indians, Sarah." "Oh, I didn't know that."

I look so cool in my Native American costume on Halloween, even though the other girls roll their eyes at my outfit. One boy in my class looks at me and says, "Hey, that's a boy Indian outfit." But I don't care. I like it way better than the other girls' dresses.

The party is so much fun. I win at bobbing for apples. Robby says it's because I have beaver teeth, but I don't care. I'm just happy to win a game.

"Mrs. Young, can I keep the candy in my desk so, I don't have to take it home? "Sure, Sarah, if you have room in there with all your toys and cards from your birthday." Mrs. Young gives me a little smirk and raises her eyebrows at me.

"Thanks, Mrs. Young."

"Sarah, why do you want to keep your candy here? Does Curtis eat it all?"

"No, my older brothers take it from me."

"Well, where will you hide the candy you get tonight for Halloween?" she asks.

"I don't go trick or treating like the other kids."

"Oh, oh, okay. I see. No eating candy in class. Agreed?" Mrs. Young says with a nod of her head, as if she already knew I would agree.

"Class, the bell just rang, so let's get our coats on, put your chair upon the desk and line up by the door," Mrs. Young announces to the class.

On the bus ride home, I sit looking out the window. What a fun day I had at school dressing up like a Native American girl.

My belly is still full of all the treats I ate and my face still has paint on it when I step off the bus. "What were you in school today, Curtis?" "A mummy." "Like Mother?" He spins around to look at me, and we both start cracking up.

We're still laughing when we get inside, but it ends quickly for me because Maisy isn't in her bed, tail wagging, happy to see me.

Mother is sitting on the couch watching her soap operas on television. "Where's Maisy?"

"She's dead, Sarah."

She might as well be telling me what we're having for dinner because she doesn't sound like she cares one bit that my dog is gone.

My eyes are getting cloudy. No, No, I won't cry in front of Mother. But then, all of a sudden, she becomes cloudy. Mother begins to disappear more and more the longer I stand there. That's it, I need to leave now because I can't stop what is happening.

No way, I'll let her see me cry!

I turn and run to my bedroom, shutting the door behind me.

"Stop runnin' in this damn house. How many times do I have to tell ya to walk, young lady? Slow your ass down *now*."

I drop my books in the middle of the floor and march straight into the bathroom. My tears and water from the sink help me get the paint off my face. I let the water run so Mother can't hear me cry. "Who the hell is runnin' water in the bathroom? Shut that off now."

Today had been such a great day. But the night is not turning out so good.

And it only gets worse because Mother and Daddy are going out. I wonder what Derek will do to Curtis and me tonight.

When I come out of my room, I see Derek is on the couch, watching me. His eyes follow me into the kitchen, and I shiver. All through dinner, I want to drop Mother's disgusting meatloaf down to Maisy, but she isn't there. Why does she have to be gone, but Derek and my brothers aren't? Dinner ends.

"Make sure Curtis and Sarah git a bath and are in bed on time tonight. Curtis had a hard time wakin' up this mornin'." Mother yells to Derek as she leaves the house with Daddy.

The truck pulls out of the driveway, and Derek goes into the bedroom while Curtis and I sit at the dinner table. As soon as Derek walks into the kitchen we see he is holding the BB gun. "Sarah, run!" Curtis takes off running.

I run after him to make sure he has a good hiding spot. I find him hiding behind a curtain in our parents' room. I pull his arm and drag him to the laundry basket. I point for him to go inside it, and I throw the dirty towels over the top of it.

By the time I have Curtis hidden, I take off running through the bathroom, our bedroom and stop in the living room looking for Derek. When the coast is clear, I take off for the kitchen and head toward the food closet.

Ping.

Derek appears from behind the front door.

I'm too late.

Before I can get inside and hide, I see the gun pointed at me.

Derek misses. I run back toward my parents' bedroom as that is the only direction I can run and the farthest place I can go.

Then, I feel it.

The BBs are hitting the backs of my legs. It feels as if someone is putting stitches all over them. Once, I cut my hand and had to get stitches. The BBs feel like the needle they used to sew me up.

Once Derek hits me, he stops shooting. This game is Derek's idea; all of them are. "Get them out here. The game is over," Derek tells Vinnie who then yells for Curtis. I walk in front of him just in case Vinnie's lying, and they shoot at us again. Derek points at the couch, and we both sit down.

"You're a damn awful shot, man, but at least you got her at the end. That was fun. Let me try!" Terry reaches for the BB gun still in Derek's hands. He yanks it away from him. "No shit for brains! If we mark them up too much, we'll have to answer to Dad," Derek yells. Vinnie and Terry slowly walk toward their bedroom, never turning their back on Derek.

The game usually lasts much longer than it did tonight because we are generally better at hiding. Tonight, I ran out of time and got caught. I rub the backs of my legs as we sit on the couch, waiting to see what's next.

"You better not tell Mom or Dad about this little game, or next time, we won't stop until we shoot the shit out of both of you," Derek threatens. "Now, get your asses to bed! We both jump up to run to our rooms. "Wait, except for you, Bucky, I want you to come here. "Curtis, get to bed." Curtis doesn't move but just stands there looking at me. "Move your damn ass now before I beat it!" This is all it takes. He hightailed it back to the bedroom while I stand there facing Derek.

"Sarah, I will hold this lighter on your arm, and I want you to tell me when it starts to hurt. Then, when it does, I'll move it. Just say the word 'stop,' and I'll move it, okay?"

"I don't want to play." I know what being burned feels like; I've accidentally done it on the coal stove in Daddy's garage too many times. "Not playing is *not* an option." He holds the flame below my wrist. It's not touching my skin, but its heat starts to burn my skin quickly.

I'm not going to tell him. I won't tell him it hurts because he wants me to.

"Sarah, is the lighter hurting you?" He keeps asking me over and over like he's not going to stop until he knows it hurts.

I'm not going to tell him it hurts. I will not tell him. I keep thinking as my teeth press together so tightly in my mouth that it feels like they might crack. I can smell the hair on my arm burning.

Derek lifts my hand and sees the burn spot on the bottom of my wrist. "Damn it, Sarah! I told you to tell me when it started hurting, and now you have a big blister there!" He puts the lighter back in his pocket. "You're too damn stubborn for your own good." He storms out of the living room, leaving me on the couch in pain.

I sit there, holding my wrist, feeling it grow hotter with every passing second.

It really starts to sting.

A blister, Derek had said. So that's what they're called. I need to get my wrist under some cold water. When Mother holds my hands under hot water, the blisters feel better when I run them under cool water.

Derek stands in the bathroom doorway as I cool down my burn. I hate when he watches me.

"Sarah, if you tell Dad what happened, I'll see how long Curtis can stand it next time. Besides, you could've moved your damn arm by saying stop, so it's your fault you got burnt. Yours!" he shouts. "Now get your sorry ass to bed."

The back of my legs hurt when I kneel to pray, all because of the BBs. "Dear Jesus, thanks for helping me protect Curtis tonight." Curtis is snoring away. "My legs and blister hurt so much, but not as bad as my heart hurts. Maisy, my dog, died today. I miss her so much. I wish I could have said goodbye. I would have told her goodbye this morning before I left for school if I knew it would be the last time, I'd ever see her. I feel so sad, Jesus. Well, good night. I better get back in bed before Derek, or one of my other brothers catches me. Amen."

That night, I dream about Maisy. It's not my usual nightmares about something my brothers do to hurt us, but about my sweet girl. In my dream, she's a puppy chasing after me as I run through the house. Mother isn't there yelling at me to stop running, so we just play. And when I'm all tired out from playing with her, I flop down on the floor by the vent near Daddy's chair, and she crawls all over me, licking my face as I laugh.

But it's only a dream because when I go to the kitchen for breakfast the next morning, I look over toward her rug, and not only is Maisy gone, but her bed is gone too. So are her bowls. It's like she was never here. My heart hurts as I realize I'll never see her again.

As soon as Halloween was over, we talked about the next holiday. Thanksgiving. At school, the kids are all talking about eating turkey. Mrs. Young teaches us about Pilgrims and this flower I had never heard of called the *Mayflower*. "Thanksgiving is a day you eat a lot and say why you are thankful." But no matter how much she tells me about Thanksgiving, I still can't figure it out.

Why? Why does my family not have Thanksgiving?

Dr. Sharon Zaffarese-Dippold
Melissa Mulhollan

Thoughts run through my mind as I wait in line at the cafeteria, trying to pick what I want to eat. I let the lunch ladies pile all this weird food on my tray. In first and second grade, I always picked the peanut butter and jelly sandwich. But today, for some reason, I want to try something else.

The meat is springy when I try to chew it but not too bad. I wish Mother would make this springy meat; it tastes kinda good. I asked a boy named Troy, sitting at my lunch table, what we were eating. "What are we eating?" he repeated my question like he didn't understand me. Then, he tilts his head back and starts laughing as he points at me, "You're funny." When I wait for his answer, he stops laughing. "Turkey, doofus." "Turkey?" I repeat. The mystery meat is sitting next to a pile of mashed potatoes and two thick slices of bread. The lunch lady dumped this light yellow stuff all over it. She'd called it gravy, but it doesn't look like the gravy Mother makes. There's a pile of corn and something with pumpkin on my tray, too.

I eat the turkey and some potatoes, but that's it. The bread looks gross with gravy on it. That's a waste of good bread. I don't like the corn either. The pumpkin smells yummy, but it tastes spicy when I put some of it on my tongue. I like the white stuff on top, so I just eat it. Lunch doesn't last very long before we are back in class. It's always like that at school. Lunch, recess, and gym class go so fast.

"Okay, class, I want you to get your notebooks out and copy this down." Mrs. Young writes the word *Thankful* on the blackboard. "*Thankful* is an adjective that means being appreciative of the benefits received and expressing gratitude. What are examples of benefits we receive from others?"

A few of the really smart kids raise their hands saying, "*friends,*" "*a new bike,*" "*food,*" "*an Easy Bake Oven,*" "*money,*" while other kids chime in listing more and more reasons to be thankful. Mrs. Young writes all the examples on the board.

I'm trying to write and listen, but it's tough to do since I write very slowly, and my letters get jumbled.

She goes on to explain how adjectives describe nouns.

"Okay, class, now in your notebooks, write about the people, places, and things you are thankful for."

It only takes me a second to decide what I'll write.

Daddy, Jesus, Lucky, Curtis, sluice fort, mud pies, and Maisy.

In the middle of my writing, "Sarah, can you come join me at my desk for a second and bring your notebook with you?" I wasn't even done yet. I put my pencil down and walk to her desk. All the other kids were still looking down at the notebook and writing. Though I'm shaking, I walk up slowly to her desk.

She looks over my notebook with a smile and then pulls a chair up next to her. She pats the chair for me to sit down. "Sarah," she says, "Can you help me read what you wrote in your notebook? I've been having some trouble reading your handwriting." *Whew!* I'm not in trouble.

I take the seat next to her. All the other kids were still busy and far away from her desk. We lean toward each other as I pick up my notebook to read it to Mrs. Young.

"My Faorite place is the sluce fort becus I go ther with my broder Curtis. We like to draw on the wall. We like to hide from pepole there to. I have a new frend from church his name is Jesus. I can pry and talk to him at nite and when Im afrad. My daddy I like to help him paint cars and work on engens in the garge with him. Curtis and I like to cath minowwos at crek by sluce fort. I mak mud pis and bak them in the son. My Maisy died bt I don't know how moder dint tell me. Im sad and mis maisey. My favrite fo…" I stop reading. "I couldn't write anymore, Mrs. Young because you called me up here to your desk."

"That was lovely, Sarah. I'm so sorry to hear about Maisy. Did you have a funeral for her?" "No, not like we did with the cats that got hit by a car. I just came home, and Maisy was gone." "I'm sorry to hear that, Sarah. Are you doing okay?" My heart starts to hurt again, so I just nod my answer to her.

Mrs. Young grabs some papers from her desk and hands them to me. "I'd like you to use these papers to practice writing at home. Have your mother help you with them and then bring them back to school completed, okay? It will help me read your work better." That answer is a big, fat no.

Mother will *never* see them.

If I tell her my teacher can't read my writing, she'll definitely take me on a trip to the bathroom sink. These papers cannot go home. *No way!* But, instead of telling Mrs. Young any of my real thoughts, I nod and take the papers back to my seat, where I stuff them inside my desk.

That night, I head straight for the garage to see Daddy when I get home. He puts the tire jack down as I hand him my new spelling list. He points at my wrist. "How did you get burned here? Was it from the heater?"

"Maybe I touched the heater as I walked by and didn't know it." I hated to lie to Daddy, but I couldn't let him leave me here.

"You've burnt your hand on that old, damned coal stove before, Dolly, but never in this spot. Dolly, are you playing with matches?" "What? No, Daddy. Never."

He doesn't stop looking at me for what feels like a long time and then says, "You know, Sarah, you can tell me if someone has hurt you."

Lying to Daddy made my heart hurt the way it did when Maisy died, but he almost left us when he saw my bruises from Mother. Even though Derek has given me this blister, I can't take the chance that Daddy will leave if I tell him the truth, so instead, I answer with, "I know I can."

Daddy stares at me for a few minutes longer, then takes my spelling list and starts going over all the words.

I have to be more careful around Daddy. He sees everything. I wish I could tell Daddy everything and know he wouldn't leave me.

It's not my fault I have bruises. I'm *not* the one who put them there. So why do Mother and my brothers want to hurt me? I wonder if other kids in my class get hurt by their families too, and they don't tell anyone. Should I tell someone?

Right! Derek would be super mean and would do something horrible to Curtis just to get at me. Then there is Mother. She put my hands under hot water when Daddy found the bruise that I didn't show him.

What would she do if I told anyone how she is mean and hurts me? *Someone, please tell me.*

Why can't I have a birthday? Why can't Mother be nice to me? Why can't my brothers be nice like other kids' big brothers and sisters in school? Why can't Mother take me to get new clothes like Elizabeth says she does with her mother, Mrs. Brenda? Why can't Mother and Daddy go to church with me like Jessica's parents, Mr. Randy & Mrs. Cheryl, do? Why can't I be like them?

Why can't I?

Forgetting where I am, I stomp my feet. "Hey Dolly, spell *capital…* Sarah?"

126

"Sorry, Daddy," I was counting all the cracks in the cement floor."

"I wondered what you were thinking about because I could tell you didn't hear me. And you stomped your feet pretty good. Is this word that hard for you to spell?"

I wish the hardest thing for me is that I can't spell the word, *capital*. I want to tell you *everything*, Daddy. Why did you have to tell Mother you would leave her if you saw any more bruises on me.

Why?

If Daddy left me here, it would be so bad for me. So, I have no choice but never to tell anyone what happens here. I could never be left alone with Mother—never.

"Sarah, honey, are you okay?"

"I'm just thinking about how to spell this word. I'm ready now."

"Capital," I say out loud. "C A...

After studying with Daddy, I walk in the house and the smell of Mother's dinner hits me in the face. She is making cabbage and ham... *again.* I don't feel like fighting with her, so I choke it down, take my bath and go to bed. I just want to be alone.

"Rise and shine, Bucky," Terry screams while he hits me over the head with the pillow to wake me up. Terry likes to hit and run in the morning. He strikes me with the pillow a few times, singing some kind of annoying song, then goes into the bathroom to do his thing to get ready for school.

Finally, he's gone. I roll over in my bed. The window has frost on the inside. It has to be super cold for that to happen. Using my blanket, I wipe a tiny spot off the window. The snow is covering the ground, but I can still see some grass in spots.

Birds outside my window are not singing anymore but, instead, are squawking and making other loud noises. I don't like it. They sound upset, which upsets me. Terry stomps through my bedroom, whacks me again with my pillow, and cracks up laughing, sounding exactly like the squawking birds.

While Mrs. Young was talking about science today, I looked out the windows and wondered why the birds were so angry. Mrs. Young starts talking about some boy named "Atom," or something like that.

I'm not really paying attention.

Mrs. Young says, "Sarah, I need you to focus on the lesson. You're not taking any notes. We are having a test on this material next week. Please stop looking out the window and look up here at me."

"I can't," I tell her. "I'm worried about the birds because they're not singing anymore."

"If you'll listen to my lesson now, Sarah, I promise to explain it to you later."

No one does anything they say they're going to for me. I'm sure she will forget.

Imagine my surprise then when during story time Mrs. Young keeps her promise. "Okay, class, are you ready?" She walks to the front of the classroom with a big, white book that has a picture of a bird on the cover. "Today, we will learn about birds during our reading activity." Mrs. Young reads, "Birds get nervous when winter comes because the ground is frozen, so they can no longer get the worms or other things they're used to eating. So, they don't sing anymore but chirp to one another, making plans to leave and fly south where it's warmer, even in winter."

"Do you mean there are places where it's warm outside all the time?" Wow, I could go barefoot and make mud pies all year if I lived there.

I am so glad Mrs. Young did what she told me she would do. I can add her to a list of people I like. I used to only have Daddy, Curtis, and Emma on my list, but I have added many new people this year. There's Jesus, Dave, Miss Sandy, Pastor Scott, Miss Lisa, both Sunday school teachers, Jackie, Debbie, Ed, and now, Mrs. Young.

And my Maisy, even though she is not here anymore. For the first time ever, I have friends and people who act like they care about me. Having friends makes me feel a little more like the other kids in my class, and I like it.

I hope it lasts.

Chapter 17
My Hands & First Mommy

As the skin on my hands turns from bright pink to red,
I bite my lip harder and can taste the blood coming from it.
I close my eyes and pray.
I keep my eyes closed and imagine my body floating away.
I'm standing there feeling the pain of the burning water
running over my hands…

"Which one of you brats woke the baby up?" Mother's face is turning purple.

Curtis goes to answer, but before he can, I say, "It was me, Mother." Curtis plays with a loose thread on his blanket.

Mother grabs my arm and drags me into the bathroom. She turns on the water and gets it good and hot. "Put your damn hands in there and if I see ya pull 'um out, you'll stand there all damn day!"

I don't even try to pull away today. What's the point? Mother always wins.

And boy, did she ever get it hot today.

"Jesus Christ. Is someone going to get that damn baby to shut up?" Terry, the light sleeper in the house, yells.

"Shut your mouth Terry," Mother shouts back as she leaves me standing there to go get Emma.

I can't believe Terry just said *Jesus* when he wasn't praying. He sounded mad. *Why is he yelling at Jesus?*

As the skin on my hands turns from bright pink to red, I bite my lip harder and taste the blood coming from it. Finally, I close my eyes and pray. "I'm sorry, Jesus, that I'm not kneeling and that I don't have my hands folded, but I need to talk to you right now. Can you help me not

129

think about how much my hands hurt and get Mother back here quickly to turn off this hot water? Thank you, Jesus. Amen."

I keep my eyes closed and imagine my body floating away as I'm standing there feeling the pain of the burning water. I see the steam on the mirror. I'm moving my body from side to side as I'm standing here.

Please, Mother, come turn off this water. My hands really hurt, and I promise I'll try to be a good girl, I want to scream to her, but I don't dare because she just gets madder at me if I ask.

She finally walks back into the bathroom with Emma and turns off the water. She glares at me and says, "I should have ya learn how to change this shitty mess in her diaper and use that as a punishment. Maybe next time, if ya want to be loud and wake her up, then ya can tend to her."

I wrinkle my face. Emma smells really bad when she poops her pants. Changing that mess would be awful. But it'd definitely be better than burning my hands. At least if I change her diapers, my nose will only hurt for a second. When Mother burns my hands, it hurts for days, and they get blisters and small red bumps on them that I have to hide from Daddy.

"Now git dressed! You two are goin' for a visit today. And if your hands are still red, ya tell 'um it's from the cold outside."

I'm squeezing my legs together because I had to pee the entire time Mother had my hands under the hot water.

She pushes past me. Thank goodness I didn't have an accident. Mother would have put my hands back in hot water again, which would be horrible because my hands hurt so much.

I get off the toilet seat, and as I unroll the paper, I'm careful not to let it touch the sores that are already starting to show on my hands. It's hard to wipe and not bump them. Now I have them on my hands *and* my arm.

When I'm done, I flush and put my hands in cold water, but I can't wash them with soap right now because the soap makes the red spots and swishy blisters sting more. I brush my teeth and head back to our room to get dressed.

Curtis looks at me and whispers, "Thank you, Sarah," before heading into the bathroom.

When Curtis comes back to our room, I'm done getting dressed. While he's putting on his clothes, we try to figure out why Mother said we were going for a visit today.

"Who do you think it is?" Curtis asks me.

"I have no idea," I answer. We never visit anyone. Our aunt and uncle visit us when they are in town. Daddy has six sisters, but we've only met one of them. When she comes to our house to visit, she always brings toys and clothes for Emma, but she never gets anything for Curtis or me.

Mother is talking on the telephone."The children are not completely ready yet. Ya know how hard it is to git 'um movin' on a school day, let alone a Saturday mornin'. Are ya close by? Okay, we'll see ya in ten minutes."

I hurry through my cereal and am almost done when there's a soft knock on the door, and someone comes in.

"Hello?"

"Come on in. The kids are still eatin' their cereal," Mother tells her. I can't see the lady at first, but then I see her. It's Mrs. A. She said she would see us again and here she is.

As soon as she shuts the front door, I quickly turn to Mother. "Could I please have another slice of toast?"

"I don't have time this mornin' to make it," Mother said quietly. However, Mrs. A. must have heard her because she pokes her head into the kitchen. "Go ahead and give it to her, Donna. I'll gladly wait."

My heart skips a beat. Mother gives me a mean look, but I don't care. Sore hands or not, I want another slice of toast this morning. The last time Mrs. A. was here, Mother was nicer, so I thought things would be different this morning when she got here. So, I ask again since Mrs. A. said we have time.

"Can I please have *just another slice*?"

"No, Sarah."

So much for that idea. I put my elbows on the table and shovel the cold cereal and milk into my mouth, stewing.

After we finish eating, Mrs. A. asks, "Children, can you come over here?" She points. "Sit down on the couch. I have something to tell you." Mrs. A. sits in Daddy's chair, looking very small in it.

I slowly sink into the couch. Curtis sits next to me, checking under the cushions, as he always does.

Mrs. A. patiently waits for him to finish and sit down next to me before she starts to speak again. "Children," she says and then puts her head down.

We wait.

Then, she picks her head back up and starts talking again. She pauses before saying, "I'd like to talk to you about something very important, and I'm unsure how to begin."

"Just say it," Mother says like she's angry for some reason.

Mrs. A. takes a deep breath, then says, "I have something to tell "This may come as a shock to you. We're going to visit a lady today who calls herself your mommy."

"My what?" I turn my head fast to face Curtis.

His head is still down and has been this whole conversation.

Mother is standing in the kitchen and doesn't look at me either.

Finally, I direct my attention back at Mrs. A. and shout, "My *what*?"

Mother snaps, "Pipe down, young lady. Ya'll wake your brothers."

"We're going to go visit her today." Mrs. A. reaches across the space between us to touch my knee, and I jerk back from her.

Nothing she's saying makes any sense. She starts talking again, and her voice sounds shaky. "This lady is your *first mommy.*"

Curtis finally picks up his head, peeking over at me for the first time since we sat down in the living room. Our eyes meet, saying nothing in return but looking at each other for a few more seconds. It's like everyone in the room is gone, and only Curtis and I are there. I am frozen.

Mrs. A. breaks the spell. "Your mommy wants you to visit today, so I'm taking you and Curtis to see her."

Mother is not looking at me, though I keep watching her. Then she turns and looks me directly in the face. "*You're* not my mother?" I'm so confused right now.

Mother just turns away without answering me.

"You have two mothers, Sarah," Mrs. A. tells me. "The one you are going to see today and the one you live with now. Your first mommy gave you to Donna, so now Donna's your mother too."

"Why did my first mommy do that?"

"Your first mommy was a singer, so she went away to make a record."

I suck in a deep breath. My first mommy made a record. I think about the music Daddy listens to in the garage on his radio and the 8-track player. He likes Elvis, Johnny Cash, and Dolly Parton the best.

He says Dolly Parton is an excellent singer and a friendly person.

"Make sure you grow up to be a nice person like Dolly Parton," he tells me all the time.

When I'd asked if he was a nice person, he'd answered, "I sure try to be, Dolly."

"Then I will be a nice person because I want to grow up to be just like you," I had told him.

"Was Daddy married to my first mommy?" I ask.

No one answers. Mother cleans Emma's tray, and Mrs. A. says, "Get your coats and your boots on children. We need to get going."

I don't move, and neither does Curtis. I have too many questions I want to be answered before we go.

I drop the question about Daddy being married to my first mommy and ask Mother, "So, you didn't have me at the hospital like you did with Emma?"

Mother's quiet for only a few seconds and then says, "No, Sarah."

"And what about Curtis?"

"No, Sarah." Mother huffs out her answer, which tells me she is getting mad about my questions like she always does.

I wonder about Travis, Christy, Derek, Vinnie, and Terry. Still, before I can ask any more questions, Mother says, "Stop askin' me questions and git goin', Sarah. It's time to go."

Curtis and I move to get our coats like we're on cruise control. I still can't believe what I've heard.

Curtis hasn't said a word, so I'm not sure if he's surprised or not or even if he understands everything that's going on. Maybe he's just doing what I'm doing right now because that's what he usually does.

Before I walk out the door, I turn my head to lock eyes with Mother. Now it makes sense. I know why she hates me. It's because I had another mommy first; *that's* it, that's why Mother hates me so much.

Turning away from Mother's mean face, I walk out into the chilly air.

Maybe this news isn't so bad after all. I already have a Daddy who loves me, and I'm thinking about how cool it will be to have a mommy who loves me, too, even though I haven't met her yet.

Daddy likes to tell us that things are starting to look up when they get better. He told Terry things were looking up when Terry passed his safety test for shop. He told Vinnie things were looking up when Vinnie passed his driver's test and got his license. He said that to Christy when she got a job and to Mother, too, when she won the jackpot at bingo. So today, things are finally looking up for me.

That means that everything is going to get better.

Chapter 18
Caseworker & Damn Bugs

"Listen, Sarah, I'm your caseworker.
It's my job to keep you and Curtis safe, and that's what I will do.
You don't have to understand everything right now.
You are children, and I will tell you what you need to know
and nothing more. Got it?"

Curtis and I climb in the back seat of Mrs. A.'s car. Daddy is walking toward us, so I roll down my window to talk with him.

"Where are you off to, little lady?" He doesn't bother asking Curtis since he never answers questions.

"We're going to visit our first mommy, the one from the hospital." Daddy moves closer to the car and the passenger-side front window. He leans down. Mrs. A. rolls the window down, and Daddy asks, "How and when did *this* meeting get arranged?"

"I apologize that you didn't know about the meeting, Mr. Connor," Mrs. A. says to Daddy with a frown. "Mrs. Connor has known about it for weeks."

Daddy scrunches up his face, taking his fingers and rubbing his chin. I've seen him make this face while touching his chin when he's puzzled.

Why is he confused that we're going to see our first mommy?

I'm worried Daddy isn't going to let us go. The way he just stands there glaring at Mrs. A, is the same look he gives my brothers when he's mad at them. "Come on out of the car and give me a hug before you go then."

Quickly, I get out of the car and jump up as Daddy leans down to scoop me up into a bear hug. While hugging me, he whispers in my ear, "If you want to ask me questions after your visit, Dolly, I will tell you anything you want to know, okay?"

135

I whisper back, "Okay."

There is nothing I can think of that I would need to ask him.

It's exciting to think about having another mother, a mommy. This mommy will take me to church like my friend's parents do. She will let me eat toast and give me more when I ask for it, and won't make me eat all the disgusting food Mother cooks. She will hold my hand, and it will be nice. She won't hold them under hot water and give me blisters. She will give me a birthday at home and bring cupcakes to school for me like Elizabeth's mom did. She'll hug me and kiss me at school and at home, especially when my dog dies. I will be able to cry in front of her, and she will be sad too when I do. She will help me with my school work and sign my papers without getting mad or calling me stupid.

I cannot possibly see what Daddy and I will need to talk about when I get back from meeting my first mommy.

Just then, Daddy kisses my cheek, and sets me back down.

I crawl into the backseat with Curtis again and close the door. Before we leave, he knocks on the backseat window to say bye to Curtis. The knocking sound makes him jump. Then he sees it's Daddy, waving and trying to get his attention. Curtis grins and waves for a few seconds then goes back to staring at the floor.

The car backs out of the driveway, and I wave at Daddy.

Actually, I do think of some questions for Daddy and once I start thinking of them, my mind can't seem to put on the brakes. How did he meet my first mommy? When did they break up? Was he at the hospital with her when Curtis and I were born like he was with Emma? Did my first mommy know Dolly Parton? Did he think she was a good singer and nice like Miss Dolly?

Mrs. A. stops my thoughts by asking Curtis and me questions that are friendly and easy to answer—what Daddy likes to call "making small talk." Curtis won't answer her, so Mrs. A. gives up and tries to talk to me.

"Sarah, do you like school?"

"No." I continue looking out the window.

"What do you like to do?"

"Nothing." I don't feel like talking to Mrs. A. I just want to think about the questions I want to ask Daddy when I get home.

Mrs. A. finally gives up and stops trying to talk to us.

I like the quiet better and go back to my thoughts.

I know Emma doesn't have this hospital mommy because Mother took her home from the hospital. Still, I start to wonder again about Travis, Christy, Derek, Vinnie, and Terry. If this lady is their first mommy, why doesn't she want to see *them*? This will be another good question to ask Daddy.

Hey, maybe... maybe Curtis and I have a different hospital mommy than everyone else. Maybe *that's* why Mother treats Curtis and me differently. She's not mean to Curtis and she's not nice to him either. But she sure is mean to me.

This is why she doesn't love me, why she doesn't love me, why she doesn't love me...

"Okay, children, we're here." Mrs. A. pulls up to the curb in front of a white house with most of the paint peeling off. The yard has a couple of empty metal cans in it, tipped over with garbage spilling out and blown across the yard.

The grass isn't grass; there are just patches of brown sticking out from the snow on the ground. The porch has a little stepladder next to the steps, which are falling off. The windows in this house look freaky. Some windows are boarded up, others have plastic on them, and a few are broken and have strips of gray tape across them to keep them together. Wow, this place looks like the haunted house in the storybook Mrs. Young had us read for Halloween. I hope my first mommy doesn't live here.

Mrs. A. says, "Don't worry, children, I will be with you for your entire visit with your mommy. I will not leave you alone with her."

Confused, I ask, "Why would we worry about being alone with our first mommy?"

Mrs. A. thinks for a minute, then nods, "Your first mommy must do some things before she may be alone with you two. It's not safe for you to be alone with her."

"Safe?" I shout, more puzzled than ever. "Why wouldn't we be safe?"

"Listen, Sarah, I'm your caseworker. It's my job to keep you and Curtis safe, and that's what I will do. You don't have to understand everything right now. You are children and I will tell you what you need to know and nothing more. Got it?" Mrs. A.'s voice had changed from kinda nice to mean in a couple of minutes.

"Are you friends with our mother we live with now?"

Mrs. A. seems to think about it before she answers. "I've known your mother, Donna, for a very long time. So, yes, I would say we are friends." Mrs. A. doesn't ask me why I asked her this question, and I don't tell her, but she sounded exactly like Mother when she talked to us the way she did just now. No wonder they're friends.

When I look at the house again, I see a woman with a little girl walking toward us through the yard. They both stop on the sidewalk, a little way from the front of the car.

"Wait here, children," Mrs. A. says before turning off the car. She then gets out. Why is she leaving us in here? She can get out of the car and meet this lady so why can't we? Looking down at the seat, I see that my hands are in a fist, just like Derek does when he's mad. Quickly I open my hands because I don't want to do anything that is like Derek. I spread out my fingers as far as they will go. I look out the window again at Mrs. A., the woman, and the little girl.

The woman standing there is about as tall as Terry and has yellow blonde hair on the ends with black down the middle. Her hair is straight and looks very stringy and thin like she doesn't have much of it. It reminds me of a teacher in our school who was sick with cancer. I hope this lady doesn't have cancer too. She's tiny and skinny like me. I can see that she's wearing a puffy purple coat. Purple is my favorite color, so I definitely like it.

Mrs. A is talking to her, but the lady isn't smiling.

The little girl with her has blonde curls that're not white like Curtis's spikes and not yellow like the lady's hair. It looks like it hangs down past her shoulders; I don't know how long it is exactly because I can only see the front of her right now. She looks like she's close to Curtis's size and is wearing white and pink boots that look dirty like my clothes. Her coat is pink and dirty too.

Pink. I huff to myself. My least favorite color ever. I guess she must be a girly-girl.

Is the tiny blonde lady my first mommy or does she know her? And who's that little girl next to her? This can't be my first mommy—she couldn't have another child here with her since Curtis and I aren't allowed to live with her, or even be alone with her.

Mrs. A. raises her voice, and the lady yells right back at her, but I can't understand what they're saying. The only word I hear Mrs. A. say is, "Responsibility."

Then Mrs. A. throws her hands in the air, turns around, and starts walking back to the car.

The lady holds the little girl's hand, but she holds up her other hand to Mrs. A.'s back and puts up her middle finger.

I've seen my brothers do this to our mother often when she walks away from them. I'm guessing it means something bad since they always do it when they're mad at her.

The strange lady mouths something to Mrs. A.'s back too, but I'm not sure what. I don't think it was nice since she has a mad look on her face.

After that, she scoops up the little girl and carries her back toward the haunted-looking house.

I watch her until Mrs. A. is back in the car.

She starts the car. "I'm sorry, children. We can't visit with your mommy today. She and your little sister have head lice."

"Wait! *That* lady is our first mommy? And we have another little sister? Is that her?"

As the car pulls onto the road, the lady and the little girl walk back inside the old creepy-looking house.

Mrs. A. jerks the car a little when I scream, "Stop the car now! Was that her? Was that our first mommy? Stop the car!"

"Sarah, stop it now!" Mrs. A. shouts back at me.

"No!" I continue screaming. "Take us back there! Take us back! I want to meet her. I need to meet her. Mrs. A., stop the car! Stop the car and turn around now!"

"Sarah, I'm driving, and you're upsetting me. Stop it before I wreck this car!" Mrs. A.'s voice booms like thunder.

Curtis doesn't say a word but watches them out the back window 'til they are out of sight.

I slide down in my seat, and a tear falls down my face. I wipe it on my coat sleeve. I'm not crying because I'm sad. I'm crying because I'm angry.

Mrs. A. says, "They had head lice, Sarah. You could catch it. You and your brother could not visit today. I'm sorry."

That's her argument? Heck, I sleep in the same room with Curtis when he gets a cough and a fever, and he sleeps in the same room as me when I get a cold. I'd even sat at the kitchen table with Daddy eating soup while he'd wiped my runny nose with his hanky. I never get sick from Curtis, and he and Daddy never get sick from me. What makes lice so bad that I can't even get out of the car and talk to my hospital mommy and little sister?

"What are head lice?" I ask Mrs. A.

"They are tiny bugs that crawl around in your hair, biting your scalp and making it itchy. They are very contagious, Sarah. You, your brother, and I could get them and bring them home to your family. They can stay in your hair, and you could take them to other students in school. So, it's really for the best that we stay away until they get rid of them."

"Will we *ever* get to see her?"

Mrs. A.'s voice is quiet. "I don't know, Sarah. I just don't know."

Everyone stays quiet the rest of the way home. When we pull into the driveway, I start to feel angrier. I feel double-crossed because of everything that happened today.

Curtis and I get out of the car without saying a word. I stomp off to the garage to find Daddy.

Just as I get to the garage, Mother comes onto the porch. Curtis walks onto the porch, but she doesn't look at him, just me. "What are ya'll doin' back so fast?"

I can tell she's not happy to see us. For some reason, this makes me madder. But I don't want to talk with Mother about it, so I don't answer.

She sighs and shakes her head. "Go on and git inside the house. It's freezin' out here. Ya don't need to go to the garage right now."

I do as she says, dragging my feet up the porch steps. I'm just about to take off my boots and put them inside the shoe bin when Daddy steps out of the garage.

"Hey there, Dolly, don't take your boots off yet. I could use your help in the garage unless you'd rather go inside with your brother?" I head back down the steps toward Daddy.

"Kids git in the house, and Sarah, leave your father alone so can git his work done without ya botherin' him."

I stop halfway down the steps, turn around, and glare at this woman who acts like she's my mother. She's not my real mother. I know now that she's nothing but a mean lady.

Her squinched-up face and tiny eyes show how angry she is right now. I'm not going to turn my head away from her. I'm on the porch step, and she is standing above me while I give her the same look she is giving me, and I don't turn away. Mother's face changes. She's no longer angry-looking, but her eyebrows go up, and she stares at me with a blank look on her face.

Daddy says in a voice so quiet, it's tough to hear, "She's a good little helper, Donna. She holds the tape, which helps me get the cars ready for painting."

"Oh, that's right," Mother says in a really smart-like voice and with an ugly scowl across her face. "She never bothers *you*. I forgot." Mother turns to Mrs. A.

"Well? Are ya gonna tell me what the hell happened or not?" Mrs. A. acts afraid of Mother as she rushes past me into the house.

Daddy's looking at me like he's worried when he takes my hand, leading me to the garage. "Your hand is all red, Dolly."

I take a deep breath and sigh. "It's from the cold, Daddy." This is the second time I've had to lie to him about getting hurt. I'm tired after everything that's happened today.

"What happened with your meeting with your mommy today, Dolly?"

I shrug and say nothing.

"Sarah, honey, what is it? You know you can talk to me about anything."

I know I can, but the way I'm feeling right now is hard to explain. I find out that I have another mommy this morning. I get excited about meeting her, a mommy who is a singer, which is why I figured I couldn't live with her. Then I get to her house, and it looks like an awful place to live. Our house is not super nice either, but we don't have garbage cans with trash all over the place. The paint on our house is only peeling off in a few places. And we can use our steps without needing a ladder to get to our porch. We have glass in our windows with no plastic or tape over them. At least our home doesn't look like an old creepy, haunted house.

Why didn't my new mommy come to the car to talk to us? She could've at least tried—I mean, she could have waved or at least smiled.

Instead, she was too busy sticking up her middle finger at Mrs. A.—right before she walked away without even looking at Curtis or me.

Now I'm standing here with Daddy, who's always nice to me, but I'm angry inside. I'm so mad I could spit nails like Daddy's nail gun. Taking big breaths is not helping me feel better. I take in a huge breath anyway. "I have so many questions about this lady they say is my first mommy."

Daddy sits on his stool, then slides mine over. He pats it. "I'm sure you have a lot of questions. I would if I were you. So where do we start?" I climb onto my stool and face him.

I don't even know where to begin.

Chapter 19
Didn't Want Me & A Car of Many Colors

But wait, what if she doesn't want to meet me?
Maybe that is why she gave me away.
"Are you sure it isn't because I'm bad?
Mother says when I get in trouble, I'm bad.
I always get in trouble with Mother, which means I'm bad.
Is that why my first mommy didn't want me?"

"What do they mean when they say she's my first mommy?" Daddy spins my chair around, stopping it to push my hair behind my ears. "Dolly, remember when Mama Cat had her kittens last year? Not the litter she had this year but the one she had last year?" I'm quiet at first and then slowly nod. "Do you remember when the gray cat had her one kitten at the same time, but she wouldn't let the kitten feed on her?"

I remember that kitty. We named her Sparkle because when I picked her up once, I had sparkles on my hand from art class that day, and I got them on her. I nod again at Daddy, though I'm not sure what this has to do with my other mommy.

"Do you remember I told you to put the kitten in with Mama Cat's litter so she would feed it?"

"Yes, Daddy, I do. Mama Cat treated the kitten like her other kittens and fed her. Mama Cat didn't even know the kitten wasn't hers."

"That's right. The gray cat was her birth mother, but Mama Cat took care of her. This is kinda like your story. Your birth mother had you, but we had to find another mommy to feed you and take care of you so you would grow up strong. That's how you and Curtis ended up living with your mother and me."

"Mrs. A. told me she was going to have to stay with us to keep us safe. Was our birth mother going to hurt us?"

"No, Dolly, I don't believe Norma would hurt the two of you now. She hasn't seen you in a long time, so Mrs. A. wanted to make sure you and your brother weren't afraid."

"Norma? That's my birth mother's name?"

"Well, yes, Dolly. Didn't Mrs. A. tell you that?"

I shake my head. "Norma had a little girl with her today. Mrs. A. said she was my sister."

"Yes, she's your younger sister, and her name is Alinda. She's a little more than a year younger than Curtis. You're the oldest, then Curtis, and then Alinda."

"So why does Alinda get to live with Norma?"

"Maybe she's trying to be a good mommy now. Do you remember what we said when the gray cat had kittens this year before she got hit by a car?"

"How did the gray cat do with feeding her kittens?" I think about that. It seems like such a long time ago.

Daddy answers for me. "The gray cat would lie on her side while the three kittens would feed on her belly. We said she did a good job taking care of her kittens. The gray cat seemed to figure it out with that litter because she was older and ready to be a mama to them. Wouldn't you agree, Dolly?"

Daddy's right. The gray cat did a much better job feeding her babies the second time.

"Dolly did Sparkle ever want to go back to the gray cat who was her birth mother, or did she want to stay with Mama Cat who cared for her?"

"No." Sparkle only followed Mama Cat around. She never went to visit the gray cat. "So, Curtis and I are like Sparkle. We have a new mother because Norma, our birth mother, could not feed us and take care of us?"

"Yep."

"And Norma is getting another chance with Alinda like the gray cat did with her new babies?"

Daddy smiles big. "Right again, Dolly."

I swing my feet back and forth. "Why does Norma want to visit us now?"

"I'm not really sure." Daddy rubs his chin. "Maybe because she's doing better and she wants to get to know you and Curtis. Do you want to get to know her better?"

I'll have to think about it.

"Well, it's not something you have to decide today."

I know Mother is supposed to be the black mama cat in Daddy's story because she feeds me, gives me clothes, and takes care of me, but she doesn't seem to like me. She's not like the other mothers I've seen with their kids at school, the grocery store, the ice cream shop, or even at church. Maybe my birth mother will do better like the gray cat did the second time she had kittens… and she'll be able to take care of Curtis and me and love us, too.

"Mrs. A. told me my first mommy was a singer. Was she pretty? Did she sound like Dolly? Did she make a record? Is her music on the radio?" I ask all of this without stopping to take a breath.

"Whoa, slow down, Dolly. That's a lot of questions all at one time. But, yes, she was beautiful when she was younger, and she was an excellent singer," Daddy sings a Dolly Parton song and stops. "And, yes, she sounded like Dolly, and I heard she did make a record though I've never heard it or seen it."

My first mommy sounds like Dolly when she sings… that is *so* cool.

But wait, what if she doesn't want to meet me? Maybe that's why she gave me away. "Are you sure it isn't because I'm bad? Mother says when I get in trouble, I'm bad. I always get in trouble with Mother, which means I'm bad. Is that why my first mommy didn't want me?"

My head bends down toward the cracked cement floor again. Daddy lowers his stool and lifts my chin. "Honey, Norma has just gone through bad times. None of it is your fault, you hear me? Promise me you will never think you are bad again?"

I cross my fingers behind my back. "Okay, Daddy." I don't want to upset him, and I always tell him the truth, but this time I can't promise that I'll never think I'm a bad kid again because I know Mother will remind me.

"What did you think of Norma when you visited today?"

"We didn't get to meet her. She and my little sister have bugs in their hair."

Daddy raises his eyebrows. "Bugs? What kind of bugs?"

"Mrs. A. called them head lice. She said we could get those damn bugs and bring them home or give them to the kids at school, so we had to come straight home. We didn't even get out of the car."

Daddy laughs so loud it echoes through the garage. "Did Mrs. A. call them *damn bugs*?"

"No, she didn't, but I'm mad about the lice ruining my chance to meet Norma, so I called them damn bugs."

Daddy finally stops laughing long enough to speak. "I know you're mad, Sarah, and I understand why, but remember our deal about not using that kind of language? Let's not use that word again—mad or not. Okay?"

I sigh. "Okay, I won't use bad words." Daddy doesn't say anything after a nod, so I keep going with my story.

"Mrs. A. got mad that we couldn't visit Norma, and Norma got mad at Mrs. A. And then, she did this to Mrs. A.'s back while she was walking away." I showed Daddy my middle finger.

He gulps, then laughs even louder. "Make sure you don't do that, okay? It's the same as using swear words. But I'm not upset, Dolly. I'm sure you don't know what it means."

"I don't, but Vinnie and Terry do it to Mother's back sometimes when they fight with her."

Daddy starts to laugh again but tries to stop. "Did Mrs. A. say when you might be going back to see Norma?"

"No."

"Well, okay, then. Would you at least like to see her again?"

"Maybe. But Norma has to get rid of her bugs first."

"My dear Dolly, I agree."

"Are you feeling a little better?"

"I *do* feel better, Daddy."

"Alrighty, then. We best get back to work."

"Yay. Can we play Dolly Parton?" "Sure can," he says as he pushes an 8-track tape into the player. Within seconds, Dolly brings the quiet garage alive with "Jolene." In a high squeaky voice, I sing along.

"That's my girl."

And just like that, we're both happy again.

Daddy lets me help walk the tape along the back-tire fender and hold it just right so he can stick it to the car.

After he finishes putting the tape on the car, he asks, as he always does, "Dolly, does that look straight to you?" When I cheerfully tell him that it does, he yells back, happy as always, "Time to paint. Let's get ready to go."

146

"Take a squat on your seat," he says, which means I need to sit on my stool on the other side of the garage, so I don't smell the fumes from the paint sprayer. "Push your stool over to car stall number two and get all your safety gear on."

I find my purple tool chest and take my special mask and earmuffs out of the top drawer. I hate wearing the painting mask, but rules are rules, and if I want to watch, I need to keep the mask on. The earmuffs don't bother me at all. Daddy, says the compression machine can hurt my ears with the loud noise it makes without them on so I wear them.

I can't find my goggles at first. Finally, Daddy points to the top of his tool bench, where the goggles sit next to his drill bit. I place them over my head, resting them on my nose.

I keep checking the garage door, trying to see out.

"Dolly, why're you constantly looking at the garage door?" he hollers to me over all the noise.

"Is it Sunday yet, Daddy?"

"No, Dolly, it's still Saturday. So, you have one day to wait. Why?"

"I'm looking for the blue bus."

He laughs. "The blue bus will come to get you tomorrow… *if* you want to go again."

My eyes get so huge that I'm sure he can see them even with my goggles. "More than anything!"

"Alrighty then we'll make sure you get on that bus."

"Do you still have my…" I look behind me to make sure no one else came into the garage without me hearing them, which has happened before. The earmuffs make it impossible to hear footsteps. "…pink slippers?"

Daddy nods while he puts a gloved finger to his lips and points to my tool chest drawer. I must've been louder than I realized with the earmuffs on. I put my finger up to my lips, say, "Shhhhh" back, happy to share this little secret with him.

The paint compressor shakes the room a little as I watch Daddy paint the car. Then, a shadow goes by the garage door. I sit still, waiting to see who it is.

I see nothing.

I have goosebumps.

I turn around, and there he is, standing behind me.

Derek.

I make a noise like Mama Cat's screams when she had her kitties.

Daddy hears me over the compressor, turns it off, and gives Derek an angry look. "Derek, do you need to startle her like that? You just scared her."

"Bucky ain't afraid of anything."

"No need to be calling her Bucky. I don't like it." Daddy is frowning, and his voice is very serious. "What do you need?"

"Mom says she needs your help in the house for a minute, something about the toilet running." He smirks at me and walks back out the door.

Daddy takes off his gear and heads for the house. "Wait here, honey. I'll be back in a jiffy."

"Okeydokey." Daddy is always so nice. I wish I could do something for him, but I'm just a kid, so I'm not sure what I can do. He's always out here in the garage working hard from early in the morning to sometimes late at night. He's so tired that most nights, he falls asleep when he sits in his big, comfy chair after dinner. I feel bad that Daddy must help Mother *and* do all this work out here.

That's it! I will paint this car for him. I jump off my stool and head to the cabinet filled with his paint supplies. I know I'm not allowed to use the compressor, and the noise scares me anyway, but maybe I can use a giant paintbrush to help him paint this car. I grab the heavy paint can with the color blue running down the side. I like blue since it reminds me of the sky and Daddy's eyes. It's also the color of our house, so it seems just right. I pry open the can with Daddy's flathead screwdriver and dip my brush. Then I paint a stripe on the side of the car going from the fender to the bumper.

As I reach the taillight, I look back up the side of the car. Right above Daddy's blue tape line, my blue line looks nice and straight. I walk back to the front of the vehicle where the paint can sets on the floor, and dip my brush inside it again. This time, I do a stripe down the middle of the hood. Cars with a line in the middle of the hood look super cool. So, I will do the same to this car for Daddy. As I walk to the front bumper, it hits me. I'm not big enough to reach the center up by the windshield.

In seconds, I climb up on the car's hood with my dripping paintbrush. I get on my knees and paint a stripe right down the middle. I scoot down to finish the stripe when I can't reach any farther. Once I'm sure I've made it wide and thick enough, I slide off the car.

Wow Daddy is going to love this. It looks great.

The car looks boring with only a blue stripe, so let's add more colors.

I walk to the paint cabinet—so many colors to choose from here. I close my eyes, count to five, then point to a can.

Green. *This will work* I like this color because it's a little darker than Mama Cat's eyes and nothing like our kitchen's throw-up color.

Without cleaning off my brush, I dip my already-blue paintbrush into the green can and repeat what I did with the blue. My new line is just as straight as the first. Now that it's on the car, the green doesn't look as dark as it does in the can. It's light green so I will call that stripe the blue-green one.

"Time to add another color." I skip to the paint cabinet. Maybe I'll use yellow, the color of the sun, and the flowers that grow in the cracks of our sidewalk that Curtis picks. And the color of my worm stand, too, of course.

The can slips out of my hand as I try to remove it from the cabinet's top-shelf. The lid flies off with a *pop* as it hits the floor. Suddenly, there's yellow paint all over Daddy's garage. Dipping the brush in the paint on the floor seems like a better idea than using what is in the can. This way, I can paint the car and clean up the floor at the same time.

The other side of the car did not have a stripe on it yet, so I start there. I make a big circle on the driver's side door, trying to make a giant sun.

Hmmm, the color doesn't look yellow—some of the other colors are mixing with it.

"My sun is an ugly color.*"*

I go back to the cabinet, careful not to step in the paint spreading on the floor and grab a new paintbrush that I dip into the yellow color. I fix my sun and make another on the back door.

My white top is now covered in splotches of all the colors that remind me of Terry's tie-dyed shirt with a bear in the middle.

Mine will look even more like his if I swirl the paint with my finger.

Oooh, it looks so neat—But wait. There's no red. That's Daddy's favorite color.

Once I get the can of red paint—which is easier because it's on the bottom shelf—I set it down, flip the lid off, and dip my brush in it. Pressing my brush against the side of the car, I walk toward the back.

This stripe will go above the green one, but I stop painting halfway. The color on the car looks more orange than red. So, I keep dipping my brush into the red and painting it over and over until I get the color closer to what I want.

When I finish, I back up toward the garage door to look at my work. *It looks so cool.*

While I swirl the red all over my shirt to mix with the other colors, I hear footsteps.

I look up.

"Wow," Daddy surprises me when he walks into the garage.

My goggles are full of paint, so I take them off to see what he thinks of the car.

He walks around the car slowly with his hand under his chin. "One, two, three stripes on this side. One blue stripe on the hood, with a few drippings of paint on both sides. Wait, let's save the best for last. We have two big suns on this side of the car."

"Did you see the red stripe? Huh? Did ya? I remembered it was your favorite color, and I got it on there, too." I'm so excited that I'm jumping up and down.

He smiles. "Yes, honey, I noticed."

"And do you like my shirt too?" Daddy points to the paint on the floor, "Did you want to put the sun on the floor, too?" "Sorry Daddy I spilled the paint, But I used that paint first on my brush so I didn't waste it and so we wouldn't have as much to clean up."

"Yes, that was good thinking. I'm proud of you."

"You love it, don't you? I just knew you would. I wanted to help you get your work done so you wouldn't be so tired and fall asleep in your chair."

He walks over, and just as he is getting ready to scoop me up and give me a big hug, he stops and points at my wet-paint shirt. "How 'bout we just high-five right now?"

My hands have paint on them, too, but we high-five anyway.

"Thank you so much for all your help. The colors are all very nice. You're the best garage mascot ever."

For the second time today, Daddy has made me feel good inside.

"Joseph! Joseph!" Mother yells from the porch. "Send Sarah inside for lunch."

"You best get inside, Dolly."

The radio is playing my favorite Dolly Parton song, "Coat of Many Colors," and it's getting harder to hear the farther I get from the garage. Hey, Daddy and I can call that car I just helped paint, *A Car of Many Colors*. How awesome is that?

Mother frowns at my shirt when I walk into the kitchen but doesn't say anything about it. I'm surprised but thankful. It could have been bad for me.

I gobble down my lunch. "It ain't too cold out for the two of ya to git outside and play today," Mother announces. Curtis and I bundle up and stay outside 'til we can't feel our fingers or toes. We had fun making a snowman and having a snowball fight.

As soon as we step inside the door, Mother yells at us. "Take your wet clothes off and put 'um in the laundry room and git out here for supper.

"Your father and I have a bowling date tonight, so your brothers will be watching you two," Mother says to Curtis and me. As if telling us that the boys will be babysitting us tonight isn't bad enough, the pile of food on my plate makes my stomach churn.

From the awful car ride to my birth mother visit that didn't happen, this awful dinner, and, now, this news...

If I hadn't had fun in the garage with Daddy, today would probably be the worst day of my life.

Chapter 20
He Ignores Me & Becoming A Young Woman

Derek lets go of my arm and turns on the water.
I'm hoping he doesn't make it too hot.
Just as I think it, steam began to fill the small bathroom.
Please don't let the water burn my body like my hands.
"Derek, I don't need the water to be so hot.
Mother doesn't make my bath that hot."
He ignores me.

"Hey, listen here, boys," Mother says, standing between the kitchen and living room so she can be heard and seen by Derek, Vinnie, and Terry. "Emma is asleep now, so ya best do like I told ya and check on her. But ya, really only need to watch Sarah and Curtis. Make sure they git a bath and git to bed by 8:30, got it?"

"Yes, Mother," Vinnie and Terry say together in a whiny voice.

She rolls her eyes turning to Derek with raised eyebrows.

"Of course, we will, Mom. I'll personally check on Emma and make sure Sarah and Curtis get their baths. Don't worry and have fun," Derek says nicely.

With Derek's response, Mother stops frowning, though she still doesn't smile.

Then she scrunches up her mouth like she always does when talking to me. "Sarah, make sure you and your brother behave yourselves tonight. Stay indoors. The ground is frozen solid now, so ya can't dig for nightcrawlers 'til spring. Ain't no one fishin' since the weather cooled down."

"Some people ice fish when it's cold out. Daddy told me people fish even in the cold by cutting a hole in the ice."

Without turning around, Mother mumbles, "Do what I tell ya, Sarah."

Daddy turns toward us. "Wish me luck, Dolly. I'm going to get the most strikes tonight."

I say nothing but just stand there looking at him.

He frowns. "Dolly, honey, are you okay?"

I shake my head and put a hand on my belly. "My stomach hurts."

Mother turns around and opens her mouth to say something when Daddy cuts her off.

"Oh, I know you don't always like Mother's food, but we all ate it and we're just fine."

Mother hits him on the arm and gives him a giggly laugh. "You think it's my cookin', huh?"

Mother doesn't laugh a lot, so it always sounds weird when she does.

"Have a good night, Dolly. I'm sure you'll feel better soon." Daddy winks and then follows Mother out the door.

What are they going to do to us tonight?

I'm glued to the carpet, listening to the sound of the truck engine revving then fading away as they drive off.

They are gone.

And now *Derek* is going to make me take a bath?

I'm going to throw up.

"Where are you running to, Bucky?" Terry asks as I head to the bathroom.

Everything in my stomach pours out of me into the toilet. I finish puking and head back to the living room. Maybe Curtis and I can somehow sneak out to the sluice fort and hide.

But then Derek grabs my arm, "You two stay out here with Curtis. I'm taking this brat back for her bath. You got it?" Both Vinnie and Terry nod at Derek.

Why is he in the bathroom with me?

"Come on, Bucky, Mom gave me strict instructions. First, I'm to make sure you get cleaned up."

"Why?"

"Mother says you are doing a shit job with getting your hair clean, so now I have to do it," he answers me with a gruff voice.

I *can* do a better job washing it, but I'm always hurrying to get out of the tub because I don't like closing my eyes in the bathroom in case a rat crawls out of the toilet. I also don't want to see that black, fuzzy stuff around the tub. So, my choices are either to wash my hair quickly or skip it altogether.

Derek can't be telling the truth because Daddy doesn't let the boys walk through the bathroom when I'm in it.

And, besides, Mother never said a word to me about Derek helping me with my bath tonight. She only said for him to make sure I got one.

"I can wash my hair. I'll make sure that I get it clean and get all the soap out. I don't need your help, Derek." I cross my arms and stomp my foot.

"And *I* say you've had enough chances to do it right, and you haven't yet, so, tonight, I'm going to help you. If you don't like it, blame yourself for never washing your damned hair right."

Derek lets go of my arm and turns on the water. I'm hoping he doesn't make it too hot. A mist began to fill the small bathroom, just as I think it. Please don't let the water burn my body like my hands. "Derek, I don't need the water to be so hot. Mother doesn't make my bath that hot." He ignores me.

"Derek, don't let the water get too hot." I say again.

"Shut up about the temperature and get undressed."

Our bathroom is tiny, and Derek isn't. There's not a lot of room for me to take off my clothes.

Why does Derek have to watch me take off my clothes? I feel like I am going to throw up again. I hope someone, or something will make it stop before I'm undressed.

Why is Derek doing this to me?

Mother *never* watches me take off my clothes. So, why is big ugly Derek?

I get up enough nerve and turn around to face him. "Get out of the bathroom, I don't want you in here." *Smack!*

My head flew to the side so hard I thought it would fall off my neck. "Shut your damn mouth and get your ass in the tub." Derek isn't yelling because everyone would hear him, but he is standing so close to me that I can smell his stinky breath.

I turn my head to face him with one hand on my cheek that feels as hot as Daddy's torch. I'm going to kick him. I am, and I am going to make sure it hurts. Then when he falls, I will grab Curtis and run away from here. I swear I'm going to do it.

"No Derek, I won't get undressed!" I yell back loudly this time, and I'm sure my other brothers can hear me in the living room. But no one comes back to check on me.

Smack!

"Shut it, because if you wake Emma, you're in bigger trouble. You are going to do what I tell you, Sarah." Derek starts to take off his belt, and I know what will happen next. "Maybe I'll go beat on your little brother 'til you get your ass in the tub." Oh, how I hate him. I know he'll do it too. I know he'll beat Curtis with his belt and buckle.

After getting undressed, I sit down on the edge of the tub and try to cover myself up with my arms so Derek can't see me naked.

He stares at me.

"Well, move it, Sarah, and get in the tub. Don't just sit there. I won't ask again."

By this point, his belt is in his hands."

Standing back up, I turn my back to Derek and put one foot in the tub. As my toes touch the water, I feel the heat. I pull my foot out.

"It's so hot," I tell him. Derek pushes me off to the side, feels the water with his gigantic hands, and yells, "It's fine, Sarah. If you don't use hot water, you will not get clean. Now get in!"

I've never heard that we have to use really hot water to be clean before.

I stand with my back to Derek. "Mother only told you to make sure I get a bath. I heard her. You don't have to stay in here with me. She never stays."

He shoves me. "Shut up and get in, Sarah."

I'm too afraid to fight with him about it anymore. He is holding his belt and has already slapped me twice, and he said if I don't get in, he will beat Curtis. Derek always does what he says he will do.

Standing in the tub, I rock back and forth while my toes turn bright pink. It almost looks like I'm wearing my church slippers from Miss Sandy, except that my feet are not fuzzy.

Derek stares at me as he blocks the door. The shower curtain is pushed back so he can see all of me as I stand there. I feel like the hamster in our classroom that Mrs. Young put in a glass aquarium—we can all look at him, but he's trapped.

The steam is going up into my nose, and I want to scream and run past Derek, but it's pointless because Daddy's not here to help me, and no one else will do anything either. Besides, what'll happen to Curtis if I don't do what Derek says?

I stand there, shivering even with the hot water and steam.

Derek points.

I sit, and my creepy brother is *still* watching me.

I don't like it.

"Well, Sarah, you *are* a girl after all."

This isn't right. Derek shouldn't be looking at me. He shouldn't be saying things like that.

I think I'm going to puke again.

Derek's right though; I ran around the neighborhood with the boys for years with no shirt on before learning I was a girl. Other girls I've seen play with baby dolls, have tea parties on the porch and wear dresses. That's not me.

Now I'm sitting naked in a tub in front of my brother, who's just told me, "You are a girl after all," as he looks over my body. When I look at him now, I feel angry the way I felt this morning. What is he looking at? Hasn't he ever seen a girl with no clothes on? His eyes are looking at the same body parts that helped the neighborhood boys see I was a girl.

Still, it's nothing like how I'm feeling right now as Derek watches me.

My legs start shaking, and my stomach feels like I just got hit by a ball, *bam*, right in the middle of my gut. It's hard for me to catch my breath. Then, while looking at my feet, dinner comes up hot in my throat. Thankfully, it slides back down quickly.

My chest looks different now that I look down at my body. These two little bumps on my chest are puffier than they used to be. They look a little like the chocolate kiss cookies the teacher gave us at school for Christmas last year. I hadn't noticed they'd grown until I followed Derek's eyes.

He kneels by the tub, coming at me with a washcloth.

"What're you doing?" I scoot as close to the far wall as possible. "I told you, I don't need you to wash me. I'm not a baby. I can wash myself.

You told me Mother only asked you to wash my hair. I can do it myself Derek." I reach to grab the cloth from him, but he yanks it away.

"Mother told me to make sure you get a bath and that's what the hell I'm doing. Do you want me to tell her you refused? Know what'll happen if I do that, Sarah?"

We both know what Mother will do.

I don't want Mother to punish me more.

Derek smirks as he places the washcloth on my back and moves his hand up and down, very, very slowly.

I'm shivering in hot water.

This isn't right—Mother *does* get upset about my hair, so maybe she *did* tell him he had to help me tonight.

I just don't know.

Derek takes the plastic cup sitting on the tub's ledge and rinses my back. Next, he washes my hair. After rinsing my hair, he brings the washcloth to the front of my body.

I go as still as a statue.

He washes my neck, my armpits, my arms, my belly, and then says, "You're becoming a young woman. Do you know what that means, Sarah?"

"No," My voice cracks. The shivering doesn't stop.

He moves the washcloth between my legs.

I try to block him, but he pushes my hands out of his way.

"I'm trying to show you what makes you a young woman, Sarah."

I already know the difference between boys and girls. I just can't talk right now to tell him, so I keep shaking my head back and forth, letting my wet hair smack my face and trying to push his hand away, but he's too strong.

"I'm going to show you how to wash your privates," He washes me with the cloth—And then he uses his hands.

"Ow." I squirm away, but there's no place to go.

He *finally* finishes when the bathwater starts to turn cold. "Get out of the tub and dry off, Sarah." I take the towel he hands me and stand up.

I wrap the towel around me but don't move. My whole body starts shivering, and my knees are knocking together.

"Sarah, come to my room."

Chapter 21
Not Some Game & I Wish I Were A Boy

A year ago, I tripped and fell on broken glass down by the creek.
"She needs stitches."
The doctor says, "Let's try to hold still, this needle will hurt the most.
What a brave girl you are. I'm going to stitch this
up now without any more
Novocain. I'm not sure why she's still feeling it, but we need to see if
she'll tolerate the stitches before we try something else."
So, I just sat there without moving, crying, or making a face as I
watched the needle go in and out. It hurt, but nothing like the pain of
being hit by BBs with a BB gun.
In the car on the way home, I pulled out all my stitches.
Before too long, I held the bloody thread in one hand
and pulled it out from the other.
"Sarah! What've ya done?" Mother yelled.
"Let's see how she enjoys gettin' her hand-stitched up a second time.
And if ya pull um out again, we won't take ya to the hospital—
I'll do it myself with my sewin' kit!"
Back at the hospital, the nurse told me it might hurt worse this time
Daddy held my other hand while they stitched me up again.
It did hurt a lot more. But I wouldn't give in and
let Mother see how bad it hurt.
Daddy and I counted the stitches as they went in quickly—one, two,
three, four, five, six. He winked after each stitch,
and I couldn't help but laugh.
After we left the hospital the second time, Mother screamed at Daddy.
"Joseph, she should be scolded, not winked at and coddled.
This is not some game…"

158

Why would he want me to come back to his bedroom? The boys don't allow Curtis and me to go in their room, ever.

Now, Derek's *asking* me to come to his room. Come to his room? After what he just did?

I don't think so.

"Sarah, get your ass back here!"

If I don't go back there, he already told me in the bathroom what he will do if I don't listen to him.

He will slap my face again, or worse.

He will beat Curtis with his belt.

He'll tell Mother I didn't listen, and she already thinks I'm bad.

I can't run away. I'm standing here in a towel, and its cold outside. The boys are in the living room. Even if I was dressed, how could I grab Curtis and get out the door before they would stop us?

Where would we go? The sluice fort?

What happens when Mother and Daddy get home? Will anyone believe me? Will Daddy leave?

I have no choice.

As I walk into the bedroom, Derek's leaning against the dresser. The boys' clothes are everywhere. Empty bottles with this brown juice are all over the dresser, and the closet door is wide open, showing an even bigger mess inside. There are two beds in the room. One is the same size as Curtis's and mine; the other is the same size as our parents'. Derek sleeps in a bed the same size as ours, except it's not a bunk bed, and there is no yellow stuff coming out of his mattress. My other brothers, Vinnie, and Terry, share the big bed in the room. Posters of girls in bathing suits cover the walls, and some are on the ceiling.

There is a small desk in the corner with no chair and one lamp on a box sitting between the two beds in my brother's room. Derek has this lamp on and has left the ceiling light off. There's a curtain in the room that makes it dark when it's closed, which it is now, but I think it's dark outside anyway because I can't see any light peeking out of the sides of the curtains. Then, all of a sudden, I hear his voice.

"Drop the towel and lie down."

"Why?"

He grits his teeth. "Because I have to make sure you're all cleaned up before Mom and Dad get home, so you don't get spanked for being dirty. Do you want Mom to spank you, Sarah?"

I gulp. "No."

"Then lie down."

He points at his bed.

Holding my towel, I do nothing but stand there staring at the wall.

"Did you hear me?" I do nothing.

"That's it, I'll go get your wimpy brother." He grabs the belt and starts to walk toward the bedroom door.

'Stop! Don't hurt Curtis too!"

I do as I'm told, dropping the towel and lying down on his bed. He walks over and then stands there, looking at me. I'm freezing; my teeth are hitting each other fast like I'm shaking in my mouth. There is a blanket on the bed that I try to pull over me.

Derek stops me. "I won't be able to check you to make sure you're clean with the blanket over you, so leave it alone," he says in a rough voice. He checks my neck, armpits, arms, and belly. "You need to lie still, Sarah."

"I need to check your privates, so don't move." I sat up straight on the bed as soon as his finger went inside my girl parts.

I can't breathe, I can't breathe! His hand is over my mouth. I try to bite his hand, but I can't move my mouth.

Stop! Stop!

I can't say anything. I can't breathe.

I feel pain like I've never felt before.

It hurts so much. *I don't understand.*

I try to move away because it hurts so bad, but Derek keeps his hand over my mouth and uses it to push me back down. His finger is still in my girl parts. I close my eyes, hoping Derek won't see the tear slide down my face.

I stare at the poster of the blonde-haired woman in the swimsuit smiling at me from the wall. I want to ask her for help, but she's smiling and not there with me. No one is with me.

No one.

I close my eyes.

Jesus.

He loves me, but since I can't get on my knees and pray right now, I sing "Jesus Loves Me" in my head.

Then, all of a sudden, the pain stops.

My eyes open, and I see him standing by the dresser.

I sit up slowly.

I duck my head and squeeze my eyes shut from the pain in my stomach and my girl parts. I watch Derek carefully, afraid of what he will do next. He's looking at his finger. It has blood on it.

"You better get your ass back into that bathroom and clean yourself up before Mom and Dad get home. I won't tell them you aren't clean if you don't tell that I checked you and found out you were still dirty."

I move slowly as I get off the bed. I feel dizzy, but I can bend down and pick up my towel without falling over. Then, I somehow manage to wrap it around me again and stumble to the bathroom.

When I get inside the door, I lean against the sink and look down. Blood is running down my legs. My heart thuds, and my throat gets tight. I'm so afraid.

Oh no, am I dying. Did Derek kill me? Don't you die after you lose a lot of blood? I didn't know what he meant when he told me I wasn't clean enough. I know when you bleed, you need stitches. I may need stitches in my girl parts now. *Oh, no, oh, no, oh, no!*

I do *not* want to get stitches in my girl parts. And I definitely can't have Daddy take me to the hospital, and there's no way will I ask Mother—she'd probably want to stitch me up herself like she threatened to do before.

When I try to sit on the toilet, it hurts bad. I start to pee and stop in the middle as it burns like fire. I try to wipe, and it's so sore down there that I decide to pat my private area with the toilet paper, but I can't tell if I got all the pee because I'm still bleeding. I keep patting my privates to keep the blood from running down my legs. I don't want to get it on the towel or floor.

I go to the sink and put a few drops of water onto the toilet paper to clean off my legs. Then, I wipe up the toilet seat, throw all the bloody toilet paper inside it, and flush it instead of putting it in the garbage to make sure no one sees it.

My hands are shaking. I put them together to pray. "Dear Jesus, it's me, Sarah. I'm in my bathroom," I whisper, so Derek doesn't hear me. "Can you please make this blood stop, so I don't have to get stitches? Amen."

I hold toilet paper on my privates and go into my bedroom to get underwear and my favorite nightgown—it's soft and long, and there's a little girl on it looking up at the stars. I take my undies and nightie back into the bathroom to get dressed. I push both doors shut, even though they don't lock. Then, carefully, I put more toilet paper in my underwear to catch the blood still dripping from my private area so I won't get it on my underwear or nightie. It has slowed a little, so maybe I won't need to get stitches. "Thank you, Jesus," I say softly.

Vinnie pounds on the bathroom door, and I jump because it scares me. I didn't hear him walk up to the door. "Get out, Sarah. I have to shit! Why have you been in there so damn long? Other people live here, too, and sometimes they need to use the shitter. I already pissed off the porch once while you took forever getting a bath. I'm not going to shit out there, too. Move it!"

I say nothing but check the bathroom to make sure there's no sign of blood. Nothing is on my legs either, so I open the door.

Vinnie shoves me out of his way, then slams the door shut.

Making myself move, my feet carry me into the living room. Derek has not come out of his bedroom yet. I wonder what he's doing back there. I hope he stays there for the rest of the night.

Standing in front of the big picture window in the living room, I stare out at the stars like the little girl in my nightie and repeat the words on my nightgown. "Starlite, Starbright, the first star I see tonight, I wish I may, I wish I might have the wish I wish tonight."

I close my eyes as tight as I can and wish tonight had never happened.

I can still feel blood dripping out of me and onto the paper in my underwear. *If I'm still bleeding, maybe I am dying.* I wouldn't care—except who would protect the animals from Curtis and Curtis from the boys if I died? Derek told me, "You are a girl after all," when he first stared at me tonight.

If this is what it means to be a girl, I wish I were a boy.

Chapter 22
I Forgot & He Hurts Me

"Don't know what I'd do without your help running errands.
Otherwise, I'd have to do it myself."
"No problem, Dad." Derek then turns to give me a crooked smile.
"Didn't mean to stop you from whatever you were going to tell Dad."
"Yes, Dolly, I'm sorry. What did you want to tell me?"
Derek stopped walking, standing in the doorway.
"I forgot what I was going to say."
It's then Derek leaves.

My private area feels worse when I move around, so I slowly climb down from my bed and head into the bathroom. When I finish, the toilet has light pink water in it from drops of blood, and so do my underwear. I can't believe it's real. I touch it on the toilet paper in my underwear.

It's all real!

Breathe. Just Breathe, Sarah, I tell myself.

No matter how many breaths I take, it will not change what Derek did to me.

I replace the bloody piece of toilet paper with another one.

Once I'm done, I stand there, staring as if I'm waiting for instructions to flush or not. I push the handle on the toilet down and listen hard to see if anyone heard it. No noise from the boys' room. I stop holding my breath and move to the sink, washing my hands and brushing my teeth as quietly as I can. After finishing up in the bathroom, I head back into my room to get dressed.

I open drawers in both of our dressers, looking for socks. At this point, I don't care whose socks they are, Curtis's or mine. I'll wear anything—finally, some socks. None of them match, but who cares? I'll have long pants on and my pink fuzzy slippers so it won't matter. I pull out a long black sock and a short white one.

When I'm finally dressed, I come out into the living room and head into the kitchen. Mother seems surprised to see me. "You're up mighty early for a day ya don't have to go to school," she says, making it sound like a question. "It's only a little after 7:00. You're dressed, too. What are ya up to, Sarah?"

Uh-oh. I don't want Mother to find out about the church. I shrug.

"I'm hungry, is all. Could I have breakfast now?"

Mother looks me over again. "Why're you dressed already then?"

"I was cold. My nightie isn't very warm," I say, which is true enough. But it's not the only reason I'm dressed.

She glares at me for a few more seconds and then nods.

Whew. I got out of that one.

I gulp down breakfast, then go see Daddy so he can make sure I get to church, but I can't move too quickly because I'm still sore.

I make it to the garage, which is super-warm and smells like him— Old Spice and paint—and all the other smells from the stuff Daddy uses on the cars. These smells help me feel better. For a second, just a second, I do not think of last night or my girl parts. Instead, I smell Daddy, and I feel… safe.

I head to his workbench. The radio's playing softly, and he's humming along.

"Hiya, Daddy!" I walk over and slap his shoulder. "I didn't miss the bus, did I?"

He jumps a little. "Oh, good morning, honey! You startled me. I wasn't expecting you this early, I guess."

"What time is the bus coming for church?" I walk to my workbench that holds my slippers. "I don't want to miss it."

"You have time, Dolly. You can hang out in here with me 'til it's time to go. Did you eat your breakfast?" I tell him I did.

"Good girl. It's cold out. You need to eat to stay strong in the colder weather. Keeps you from getting sick. I see you're all dressed nice and warm, too. Good girl. Maybe you should leave the slippers here and just wear the boots you got on your feet right now since it's so cold and snowy outside."

I didn't like that idea at all. "What if I carry my slippers and put them on inside the church. I can take them off before I leave, just like I do at school with my sneakers and boots?"

He puts his finger on his chin. "How did you get so smart?"

"You think I'm smart?" I push my shoulders back, standing a little taller.

"You betcha, honey. You can do anything you want to do. Remember that, okay?"

"I will, Daddy."

"Good." He squeezes my shoulder. "You have under an hour before the church bus will get here, so can you help me by holding the tape for this old Mercury Monarch?"

"Yupper." As I hold the tape, I think about telling Daddy what Derek did to me last night. "Daddy, can I tell you something?" "Sure sweetheart, you can tell me anything." "Last night Der…" It's then I see him as if he came out of nowhere.

Derek's here.

"Hey Dad, do you need anything from the store? I'm heading into town." "Nope, I'm good Bud, thanks for asking. I appreciate how helpful you always are, and you save me many trips to the store. Don't know what I'd do without your help in running errands. Otherwise, I'd have to do it myself." "No problem, Dad." Derek then turns to give me a crooked smile. "Didn't mean to stop ya from whatever you were going to tell Dad." "Yes, Dolly I'm sorry what did you want to tell me?" Derek stops walking and stands in the doorway. "I forgot what I was going to say." It's then Derek leaves.

"Ah, it happens to me all the time, Dolly. Well, if you remember, be sure to tell me. Thanks for helping me tape off the car. I'm going to do my Sunday morning cleaning and paying bills now."

He pulls his reading glasses out of his workbench and uses this little machine he calls a calculator. I watch him add numbers and then write down the answers.

Suddenly, I get an idea. "Daddy, how many cups of worms would I need to sell to buy one of those calculators?"

Without looking up or stopping what he's doing, he says, "You can use mine anytime you like."

"No, Daddy. I need it for school because math is not my thing, and I hate it. A calculator can make me smarter at math, so I really need one.

You said I'm smart, but math makes me feel stupid." He stops what he's doing.

I go to put my head down to stare at the cracked cement floor like I always do when I don't want Daddy to look at me, but he catches my chin before I can.

"When are you going to learn that you don't have to look away when you need to tell me something, Dolly, honey? So, school is tough for you. It's no wonder. Other kids started in kindergarten, but you started in first grade. They had a whole extra year to learn all those lessons before you ever got there. You just need time to catch up, is all. And you will. Meanwhile, you can't have a calculator in school at your age. You need to learn to do the adding, subtracting, multiplying, and division without it first. Trust me, Dolly."

I don't like Daddy telling me, no, but I believe him. "Okay, if you say so."

"Daddy, do you want to get on the blue bus and come to church with me?" I remind him that he can listen to Miss Lisa sing like Dolly.

"I would love to go with you, but I have too much work to do. How's about you say a little prayer for me?"

"Okay. My Sunday school teacher showed me how to pray." "Wonderful.".

"Come over here so I can fix your hair." He moves my bangs from my eyes. He told me not too long ago that those metal nails are called bobby pins. The name is silly, but I'm glad I finally know what they are called. I was super happy they weren't called "Robby pins." That kid gets on my last nerve.

When Dave waves at me, I walk in front of the bus, and he opens the door and says hello in the same happy voice he used the first time I met him. I climb up the steps and look around. I see Miss Sandy and head toward her seat when the girl with red hair sitting behind Miss Sandy says, "Hey, you can sit with me."

I look behind me, expecting to see someone else who got on after I did, but there's no one.

She's talking to *me*.

So excited, I head over to sit with her but look at Miss Sandy before sitting.

"Go on, child. I don't mind."

While sliding in the seat with my new friend, I tap Miss Sandy on the shoulder. When she turns around, she does her little winking trick at me again, and the girl in the seat and I laugh. I smile and wave at Miss Sandy.

I have *another* new friend.

"My name's Paula. What's yours?" She scoots closer to the window, giving me more room in the seat to sit down.

"Sarah, Sarah Bailey." I smile and then try to cover my big teeth with my lips.

"Do you live back there, Sarah, Sarah Bailey?" We both laugh.

"It's just Sarah," I shrink down in my seat, hoping she won't say anything mean about my house and Daddy's junk piles and cars.

"I bet you have a lot of fun playing in those cars," she pretends she is turning a steering wheel.

I'm in such shock that I'm quiet while figuring out what to say.

"Or aren't you allowed to play in them?" Paula shrugs.

"I'm allowed," I tell her all about using car parts for my mud pie ovens and the forts I have made with the car doors. I also tell her about the hiding places for Mama Cat and her babies that I find using the old cars. I don't mention Curtis being the number one reason they needed a hiding place. I only tell Paula I moved her and the kittens, so nothing terrible finds them.

When we get to church, I take a deep breath. I'm *finally* away from Derek, Mother, Vinnie, Terry, and school, and I'm at a place where I smile and where people like me.

Paula skips toward the building, but I stay back with Miss Sandy. Running with her will not happen for me today because of what Derek did to me. She's twelve, so she's in a different Sunday school class. I don't see her much when we are at church, but I still hope she isn't mad at me.

"Sarah, why didn't you run in with Paula? I was fine with you sitting with her and staying with friends today, although I do love your company." "I didn't feel like running today, I hurt my ankle last night." "You hurt your ankle child, how did you do that?"

I pause so I can come up with a story. Miss Sandy tilts her head, and it looks like her eyes get bigger as she waits for my answer. "Um, when I was running around the um, house, I twisted it." "Do you want me to have someone at church check it out?" "Nah, I'm okay, just as long as I don't run." "Okay, Miss Sarah, but let me know if you change your mind, okay?" "Yup, I will." She stops asking me questions, so I think she believes me.

A lady in a big straw hat stops and asks Miss Sandy, "Are you staying after church for play practice and lunch?"

I wait for Miss Sandy to answer because I'm now really interested in this play and food.

They have plays at school, but I never want to be in them because I don't like people looking at me. "Yes, I'll be staying to volunteer," Miss Sandy replies.

During the climb up the church steps, I ask Miss Sandy, "I rode the blue bus here. Am I staying and eating lunch too?"

She stops in the middle of taking a step. "Oh, dear, Sarah. Will that be a problem? Do you want me to call your mommy and tell her you'll be late today?"

Definitely not! If Miss Sandy calls Mother, I'll be in trouble because she'll know I left. If Miss Sandy doesn't call, I'm in trouble too because if we are eating lunch at church today, Mother will know I'm not home when she yells for me to come inside and eat lunch. Either way, I'm doomed.

But I think I should take my chances with Mother when I get home.

"No, thank you, it's okay."

"Are you sure, child?"

"I'm sure."

During Sunday school, Mrs. Krandle mentions play practice today and lunch. "If we end up with more children who wish to participate than there are parts, we will add parts. No child will be excluded from the play if they want to be in it." Debbie, Jackie, Ed, Jessica, and a new kid, Milton, look excited by this news.

"Sarah, are you staying for practice today?" Jackie asks.

"Yes," I say, but only because I heard Miss Sandy say she is staying.

"Yay!" Debbie, Jackie, and Jessica shout. But I'm not excited because I don't want to be in a play.

Mrs. Krandle continues, "Here is the list of roles for children in your age group. Look them over, and then I will write down the names of the volunteers next to all the parts."

Milton raises his hand so high that his butt lifts off his chair. Mrs. Krandle calls on him. "What's for lunch?"

"The ladies have been hard at work in the kitchen making hot dogs and macaroni and cheese from scratch, with brownies for dessert. How does that sound?" she places her hands on her hips, waiting for our answer.

The kids all shout, "Yum!" "Yay!" "Yabba dabba doo!" and all kinds of other cheers as my stomach growls.

Then, they look over the roles. Debbie wants to be a person named Mary.

"Figures." Jackie rolls her eyes. "Well, I'm going to be an angel who tells the shepherds about the birth of Christ." Whatever all that means.

Jessica is still deciding.

"I'm going to be Joseph!" Milton yells. "Hey, Ed, why don't you be a donkey in the play?"

Ed and Milton start laughing.

"Um, Jackie? Do you have a copy of the story about the birth of Jesus I could read?" Her eyes get huge.

"It's, um, been a long time since I heard it. If we're doing a play on it, I want to make sure I look over the parts before I volunteer for one of them."

"Good idea." Phew, I did a good job coming up with that excuse. Jackie gets a book from Mrs. Krandle and brings it back to the table. Jackie begins going through the book. "We're gonna skim through it so we can read about all the important parts," Jackie tells Jessica as she leans over to look through it with us.

"Debbie wants to be Mary. Oh, boy. That's a *lot* of talking," Jessica says, pointing to the pages. "I want to be Innkeeper Number Two because he only says one thing." Jessica explains why she picked her part like she's only talking to me. Hey, there's an Innkeeper Number Three. So maybe Jessica and I can be Innkeepers together. Then I won't have to be alone. But that still means I would have to speak in front of people and have them look at me, which will not happen.

"I want to be the angel, Gabriel," Jackie tells Jessica.

Ed says, "The angel was a boy, Jackie."

"It's a play, Ed," Mrs. Krandle interrupts. "It doesn't matter who plays which part."

Jackie smirks at Ed.

"What part do you want to play, Sarah?" Debbie asks.

I take in a deep breath, look at the picture of Jesus on the wall, before I blurt out my answer. "I don't like to talk in front of people, I don't like people looking at me, so I don't think I want to be in the play."

Mrs. Krandle walks to our table and leans down in front of me. "Sarah, since Debbie, Jackie and Jessica really want you to be in the play with them, you can be an animal in the manger where Jesus is born. That way, you can wear a costume, and no one will see you and you won't have to talk. How does that sound?"

"I don't want to be in the play," I whisper.

"Awwwww." Debbie, Jackie, and Jessica shake their heads as they make that sound.

Mrs. Krandle shushes them, then whispers, "Sarah, I won't force you, but I really think you would love it if you gave it a chance."

"No, Mrs. Krandle, I know I wouldn't love it," I whisper back. I told you, I don't want anyone looking at me, and I don't like to talk in front of people."

"I assure you, in the costume, no one will know who you are, and the animals don't talk," she reminds me again.

Jessica points to a picture of the animals standing in the manger in the book. "That's what you would do, Sarah. You just stand there in a costume. Most people will want to watch Baby Jesus, Mary, Joseph, the wise men, and angels but not the animals."

Ed and Milton flap their arms. "Come on, Sarah, don't be chicken!"

My head snaps in their direction. *Chicken? Me?* These boys aren't from my neighborhood. If they were, they would *not* have called me chicken. They've never seen me outside, running through the pricker bushes, playing around the junk cars, jumping into creeks, and climbing into sluice pipes.

I'll show *them* chicken— "Okay, I'll do it." Ed and Milton high-five each other.

Debbie says, "Yay!" again.

Jackie claps.

Jessica bounces in her chair, and Mrs. Krandle nods and walks away, grinning.

The only thing that would make being in the play even better is if Daddy came to watch it. I'll have to ask him.

When Sunday school ends, and we're done singing and worshipping in the big room with the adults, we head toward a huge room near the kitchen to eat lunch before play practice begins. I walk down the hallway with Miss Sandy while the other kids run ahead of us. I stay behind because I still hurt too much to run and want to be alone with Miss Sandy to talk about something that has been on my mind ever since Lucky almost died.

"Miss Sandy, what happens to people when they hurt animals?" Miss Sandy stops quick. After I walk a few steps past her, I stop too. "Why do you ask me that, Sarah?" "Um, I know someone who hurts animals. Does that mean that Jesus doesn't love him?" "No child, Jesus loves everyone. Maybe that person is hurting inside or maybe someone is hurting them, and that's why they are mean to animals. Who is this person, Sarah?" she puts her hand on my shoulder.

What did I just do? I could never tell her it was my brother. "Um, it's a kid who lives in our neighborhood. He tried to drown one of Mama Cat's kittens, but I saved her. I just wondered if Jesus loves him too." "Yes, He does, honey." We are quiet for a few more seconds and almost to the big room.

"Sarah, you need to tell your mom and dad about this neighborhood boy. And maybe you should stay away from him too. It doesn't sound like he's a very nice person. Has he hurt you, child?" Oh gosh. I can feel all the blood leave my face. I imagine I look like the ghost costumes from Halloween. Hurt me? Stay away from him?

Maybe I should tell her that he's my brother…

Then, again, maybe not.

171

Chapter 23
Another Pair & No One to Tell

I lost a mitten once because of that hole in my coat pocket.
Mother, of course, noticed when I came home with only
one on my hand after school.
She told me she wouldn't buy me another pair, so I had to wear them on
the one hand and then switch it to the other when it got cold.
It didn't fit right on the one hand, but it helped keep it warm anyway.
When Mrs. Young saw me put on just the one mitten,
she got me another pair.

"Are you hungry," Sarah?

It's then I smell the food. "Yum! What's that smell?"

"Lunch Sarah, are you ready to eat?" "Yes, I am Miss Sandy. Yes I am."

We sit down to eat at some really long tables. In front of each seat is a white Styrofoam cup like we use for the worms in my stand. "Awesome, I love red Kool-Aid," Jessica drinks from her cup and says, "Ah!"

I take a big swig, and boy, I love this stuff! I drink it fast and suddenly burp. "Excuse me," I say quickly and duck down a little. I'd burped at home, and before I could say a word, Mother whacked me on the head and said, "Ya say excuse me at my table, ya hear?"

But Debbie, Jackie, and Jessica start cracking up, and they don't sound mean, so I laugh with them.

I love my Sundays at church because it's like the garage and the creek—a whole different world where I'm happy and can be myself.

After drinking the Kool-Aid, Debbie has a big red ring above her lips, making Jackie, Jessica, and I laugh even more. Debbie isn't mad when we tell her why we are laughing. She just wipes her lip on her arm and laughs with us. We are all laughing with Debbie, but not at her. It's different for me at school. Kids make fun of me to be mean, and then everyone else starts laughing.

Lunch is hot dogs and macaroni and cheese. Mother makes these, but they don't taste near as good.

Debbie tells me the mac and cheese here is made from scratch. I give her a confused look. She then tells me it means it's homemade. After my face doesn't change, she says, "It didn't come from a box, Sarah."

Jessica brags, "The mac and cheese are my Babcia's recipe."

"What is a Babcia?"

"It's my mommy's mom—my grandma—who we call Babcia because it means grandmother in Polish. She is Polish."

"Oh," is all I say.

I have no idea what a grandma is or what Polish means, but I want to look smart, so I act like I know what she is talking about. I must have done that well because Jessica did not give me any funny looks. That's what people do to me when I say something stupid or dumb.

Babcia is one of the ladies who made the food and handed it out to us. Jessica jumps up from the table opening her arms. "Hi Babcia." Like my Daddy does, Babcia hugs Jessica tight, kissing her forehead.

Watching Babcia hug and kiss her makes me feel something inside that I can't explain. Why don't I have a Babcia? Why do I only get Daddy and my friends not only have both a mother and daddy to love them, but also a Babcia?

Why can't I have *that*?

Debbie is shoveling the mac and cheese into her mouth now, saying, "Mmm, mmm," over and over. I take a bite. *Wow!* This stuff is super good. It's now my fifth favorite food. I cannot stop eating it, just like Debbie. We look at each other with our mouths full, looking like two chipmunks, and giggle.

After lunch, we go to the stage in the big room and talk about the setup for the play. A twelve-year-old girl, also named Sarah, gets the part of Mary. Debbie is bummed out, but Jackie gets to be an angel. Debbie and Jessica both end up being Innkeepers. Ed and Milton become wise men, and an older boy gets to play Joseph. And I get to be one of the sheep. I will wear a costume, and I don't talk, just like Mrs. Krandle and my friends told me. Play practice is so fun.

173

I go over to Miss Lisa while she's getting the microphone set up and tug on her shirt. "At school, I get my Halloween costumes at the nurse's office out of a closet. Do you have a closet like that here so I can get a sheep costume?"

Miss Lisa bends down and puts her hand on my back really lightly. "I will have your sheep costume for you, Sarah."

"You know my name?"

"Of course. I know all our church members."

I'm now a member of this church? I smile again. My cheeks are actually starting to hurt. I have never smiled this much and for such a long time. No one hurts me or makes fun of me here. Everything is fun, and I have friends. This is all new for me, and I like it.

After practice, I say goodbye to all my friends and climb onto the church bus to go home. I want to sit with Miss Sandy on the ride home, but Paula asks me to sit by her again. I liked sitting with Paula on the way to church, but I'm too worried right now, wondering what Mother will do to me when I get home. She has to know I was gone for sure today because I ate lunch at church and probably missed it at home.

I see Paula. While I'm trying to decide whether to sit with her or Miss Sandy, another girl makes up my mind for me and sits with Paula. So I plop down in front of them, and Miss Sandy slides in beside me.

Once again, I lean my head against the bus window to talk with Jesus. This time, I say the words in my head, so Miss Sandy won't know why I'm worried. Then, I fold my hands and close my eyes.

Dear Jesus, please don't let Mother find out I was gone and at church. I don't want her to make me stop going there. Please don't let her punish me for not being home for lunch. Amen.

I open my eyes to see Miss Sandy looking at me. "All better?" she asks.

"I hope so."

"See ya next week!" I say quietly to Dave and Miss Sandy. Then, slowly, I walk down the bus steps. The doors close, and the bus pulls away. I have my slippers tucked inside my coat.

I head toward the garage to drop off the slippers and bobby pins, looking at the house as I walk. So far, so good.

I make it inside the garage. Daddy's in stall number two on his stool doing something with a tire rim when I walk in. Fleetwood Mac is playing on his 8-track tape player. Before I give him a hug or a kiss, I ask quickly, "Is Mother mad I missed lunch?"

"Well, hello to you, too." Daddy laughs. "Mother didn't even make lunch for you today, so don't you worry your pretty little head none."

Wow am I lucky. Or maybe it's *not* luck—perhaps it's Jesus working his magic again. That guy keeps surprising me. I'm so happy I found out about him. Whenever I pray to him, my prayers come true.

That first Sunday school teacher told me, "He sees everything."

Does he see Mother, Derek, and my brothers all hurting me? I need to pray to Jesus to make Derek stop. To make him go away. I hope he works on it as fast as he did with Mother and me missing lunch today.

Derek.

Thinking about him makes me feel like I wanna throw up.

Derek has used any chance he can to check me all week.

I don't fight him.

I don't move.

I don't make a peep.

I just do what he tells me to do.

I don't even like to eat anymore.

My favorite foods used to taste good. Not anymore. I can't even finish my toast and cereal at breakfast. It feels like it will come back up my throat because I can't get away from his smell.

It is *everywhere.*

It used to only be in the house, but now I smell him when I leave too.

Mother was gone this week visiting my sisters and going to the store with Daddy. I used to say I wished Mother would leave the house more often, and now I am sorry for ever having made that wish.

It's been a while since Derek tried to give me a bath, but when I take one, I scrub and scrub, hoping to get clean enough, so Derek will leave me alone. He never has blood on his finger anymore when he finishes checking me, but he still keeps telling me I'm dirty. How am I supposed to know what makes me clean and dirty if he only *tells* me I am dirty?

There's no way I am going to ask him to show me.

I want to ask another girl how to get clean, but who? Asking Mother is a big, fat *no.* I could never ask my sister because she's way too close to Mother and tells her everything. I could ask Mrs. Young, but the other kids might hear us talking and tease me. Mrs. Krandle is kind, but I don't think I could ask her something like this. I could never ask Debbie, Jackie, or Jessica because this is the first time I've had real girlfriends, and I don't want to mess it up. I think about asking Miss Sandy, but how?

I know I have asked all these people questions before, but this question is different. It's how it makes me *feel* when Derek touches me, like something is wrong with me, especially when he says I'm not clean. It's different from asking if the Pastor's name was Pastor or Scott, about Jesus, or about a Babcia.

I guess that means there's no one I can ask.

I ask Daddy about everything, and he explains it all to me. But asking him this question is something I can't do right now.

I tried telling Daddy the other day, but Derek heard me.

Then I hear Daddy calling my name, but it's as if I can't speak.

"Dolly?" "Sarah?" Daddy reaches out and shakes my arm like he's trying to wake me up.

"You were zoned out for a while. Where did you go?"

"I'm right here with you."

"Well, what you were thinking about?" I come up with another question I have wanted to ask him.

"Daddy, how did Jesus get up to Heaven?"

Daddy told me Jesus died on a big cross like the one on top of the church. At first, I thought the cross was a math sign, but he explained that it's actually called a cross and, "looks an awful lot like a math sign." After that, I knew Jesus couldn't like math, but I still call it a math building sometimes.

"Why did he want to die that way, Daddy? Didn't it hurt?" I asked.

He explains to me that Jesus didn't choose to do it, but some men were afraid of his power and made him get on the cross and left him to die. "Jesus died for our sins. This way, we can all go to Heaven when we die."

"So, when I die, I will see Jesus in Heaven?"

"Yes, you will. Everyone who dies goes to Heaven."

"*Everyone*? Even pets?"

"Yes, Dolly."

"So, Maisy is up with Jesus, and I will get to see her again when I die?"

"Hold on there, sweetheart. That's not going to happen for a very long time. You have a lot to do while you're here on earth, Dolly." "Like what, Daddy?"

"Jesus has a plan for you first. Something you're supposed to do while you're here before you leave for Heaven."

Smiling, I remember my Sunday school teacher had told me the same thing. I knew Daddy was smart.

"Daddy, what's Jesus's plan for you?"

"My role is to help people fix their broken-down or scratched up cars."

I looked at the taped-up car. "Jesus wants you to put racing stripes on some people's cars?"

Daddy laughs loudly. "I guess so, Dolly. I guess so."

"The teacher told me I had to figure out my plan for myself. How do I do it?"

"You'll figure it out when you get bigger. Just listen to Jesus. You can feel 'um in your heart and you'll know what to do, always," he pats my heart.

My Daddy is the best at helping me figure things out. I want to grow up to be like him.

Maybe that's what Jesus wants me to do.

I picture Jesus hanging on a cross and dying for me.

Why does my heart hurt so much thinking about it?

Now I know that when I pray, I'm never alone.

Chapter 24
Mustangs & The Twist

Mother would never let me get a horse.
But Daddy said when I am sixteen, we'll fix up a car together for me.
So, if I can't have a horse, I'm going to ask for a Mustang hot rod car,
and to thank him,
I'll name it Daddy.

Mrs. Young marks off the days on the big wall calendar at school. Everyone starts counting the days to Thanksgiving break.

I don't care about Thanksgiving break but I'm excited about going to the library today. "Let's line up and get ready to go," Mrs. Young instructs us.

My favorite library book of all time—has horse pictures in it, called Mustangs like the hot rod Daddy worked on in his garage.

Trying to be sneaky and not get caught, I tuck the book under my arm and act like I'm looking on the shelves for other things to read.

Then, when it's time to leave—*bam,* I pull out the horse book and drop it on the checkout counter next to the librarian and Mrs. Young.

"You wandered around all period looking at the shelves, and you come back with this book again?" the librarian says with many wrinkles all over her face. "Sarah, you sign this book out every time. I've told you before you have to find something new to read so other students can have a chance at reading this book too." The librarian takes the book from me and sets it on the cart behind her. My plan didn't work—I got scolded anyway and she told my book away.

I bit my lip so hard, embarrassed because she yelled at me about it in front of all the other kids. There are more pictures in that book than there is writing, and since I can't read very well, it is the perfect book for me. I knew most of the words by heart, and I'd look at the pictures and dream of riding away on one of the horses whenever Mother would get mad at me.

In my dream, the horse lived in a big red barn behind the garage in place of Daddy's junk metal pile. He and I would, of course, paint it red since that was his favorite color. I'd get to sleep in the barn with the horse whenever I wanted to get away from my family. I'd lie on the horse's hay, which I would get from Mr. Bob's goat pen.

The next day when I get to school, I walk into class, and sitting on my desk is the same horse book. It looks like it's brand new and not like the one from the library. A note is written on the inside cover when I open it up. It says, "Dear Sarah, this book is yours to keep. Now you can sign out different books from the library." It's signed, "Mrs. Young." I hug it and put it in my desk, so the other kids don't see it and take it from me or make fun of me for having it. I slip my church bookmark out of my desk and inside the cover. When Mrs. Young and I look at each other, I mouth the words, *"Thank you,"* she mouths back, "You're welcome." Daddy was right; I do have a really great teacher this year.

Mother would never let me get a horse. But Daddy said when I am sixteen, we'll fix up a car together for me. So, if I can't have a horse, I'm going to ask for a Mustang hot rod car, and to thank him, I'll name it *Daddy*.

I get out that book for the rest of the week and look at it whenever possible.

My first book.

At supper on Saturday, Daddy tells Mother about his weekend plans. "Donna, I'm going to need Sarah's help tomorrow with taping off the Chevy. I promised to have it done by the end of the day."

"Can't one of the boys help you? She doesn't need to be in the garage with you all the time. It's no place for a girl."

"Sarah does a good job with helping me tape off the car, and I can't always count on the older boys being around. And Curtis never wants to work with me, so you'll have to be okay with Sarah coming out there." Big, long sigh, but she doesn't say *no*.

"Be sure to send her out in the morning after breakfast." Daddy gets up from the table and heads toward the recliner, where he dozes on and off for the rest of the night while I lay by his chair on the floor until bedtime.

179

I've never eaten breakfast so fast as I do the next day. "Good morning, Daddy!" I say as I burst into the garage.

"Good morning, Dolly. Would you like to help me before you leave for church?"

I knew it! I knew it! Daddy only told Mother he needed my help to get me out of the house so I could go to church.

As soon as the blue bus pulls up, Dave opens the door and off to church we go. Once again, we stay late this week for play practice and lunch. So far, Mother hasn't figured out where I go every Sunday. Maybe I can stop worrying about it so much. Then again, maybe not. If she found out about the church and how much I liked it, she would prevent me from going just to be mean; I'm sure of it. You know what? Even her punishments wouldn't stop me. I'd find a way to get to God's house, no matter what.

I feel bad about leaving Curtis at home every Sunday, but Mother might find out about church if he came with me. *But why hasn't he asked me where I am when I'm not here?* Maybe Curtis thinks I'm in the garage with Daddy. He knows I hang out there whenever I can, and he usually doesn't go to the garage to look for me.

We go back to school for three days after that Sunday, and then we are off for the Thanksgiving holiday. Before our break begins, on the last day of school, the teacher tells all of us to enjoy the turkey and our time off. Mother doesn't make that springy meat but something stinky she cooks this time of year—venison.

"Do you think he would miss out on a chance to use a gun?" *A gun? Derek has a gun?* "Why does he need a gun?" I blurt out.

Vinnie and Terry look at me like I have two heads. "Sheesh, Sarah, how the hell else is he going to shoot the deer to get the venison?" Terry growls at me like a dog. The boys had been talking about hunting deer on Monday all through supper. Thinking about them killing an animal makes eating another of Mother's awful dinners worse for me, but being reminded that Derek has a gun means I can't eat another bite.

Suddenly, I think about Emma's book *Bambi*, and it hits me. That crazy Mrs. A. told Mother I was a hunter and not a Bailey? Of course, she had no idea what she was saying.

Whenever I've prayed before, Jesus worked really fast. Not this time, though. I never thought in a million years I would say that I would

180

rather be at school. This break has been too long, and Derek has been worse than ever. Mother has been gone the past couple of days; she took Emma to Christy's house to visit one day and went shopping the next. Derek called me into the bedroom both days. He has used the same excuse—telling me he had to make sure I was clean because if I wasn't, Mother would get mad. I want to ask Mother, but I don't want to get in trouble; I just want him to leave me alone. Monday can't get here fast enough.

I go out to the garage to see Daddy sweeping the floor. All his tools and stuff are put away. Oh, no! It's Sunday—I must have missed the bus. "Daddy, did… did I miss going to church?"

He tilts his head. "No, honey. Today's Saturday. Church day is tomorrow. Why do you ask?"

"Because you're cleaning up the garage. You said you do your cleaning and bills on Sundays, so why are you cleaning today if it's only Saturday?"

"Ah. I see why you're confused. I'm having the band over tonight to play. Gotta make room and get the garage all spiffy. Tonight, might be our last chance to get together before it gets cold until spring."

My eyes widen, and I rock on my feet. "Can I help you get the garage ready?"

"Of course, you can! You're my little garage mascot! And, tonight, I hope you'll be my musical mascot, too, and come out and watch me play. For now, how's about we practice while we work?" Daddy puts on some Johnny Cash and starts singing "Folsom Prison Blues." Then he dances over to me, takes my hand, and spins me around like a top. We dance and sing and spend the rest of the day cleaning up.

Daddy pulls the cars out, making a big, open space in the middle as a stage. His band has five guys in it. Daddy plays guitar and does most of the singing.

They play more in the summertime when the weather is nicer. Many people come to our house to listen to them play, standing outside and dancing in our driveway.

We set up chairs, and when Mother gets home, we fill Daddy's fridge with beer. Then, Mother makes us bologna sandwiches for dinner.

They don't taste too bad.

"That's all I have time to make for ya. I got to git myself and

181

everythin' else ready for tonight." She always takes a lot of time doing her makeup and hair and is much nicer to us on days when the band plays.

"Mother, could we have some snacks and drinks too?"

"No, they're for the adults. Ya had sandwiches. That's plenty. When I was a little girl, we didn't get anywheres near as much as you two get. You're ungrateful is what ya are."

Terry is on the couch listening. "You were little before?"

Mother cackles, rolls her eyes and leaves for the garage with her tray.

There's no point arguing with her. I don't want her to keep me from going out to watch them play.

Now that everything is set up, Mother is trying to take care of Emma and get herself ready. "Hey Derek, will you get their bathwater runnin' and make sure they git in there and wash their hair?" She points at Curtis and then me. "Curtis's hair looks greasy."

"Sure," Derek says a little too quickly.

Mother looks at him funny. "What? No bitchin' when I ask ya to help? Ya used to always complain."

Instead, he doesn't answer Mother but turns to Curtis and me. "Who wants to go first?"

"Not me!" I say a little louder and sassier than usual. I don't want to get one at all.

Mother jerks her head toward me but only stares for a second before going back to what she's doing.

Derek takes Curtis to the bathroom but keeps his eyes on me the entire way out of the living room. My skin feels like it's moving.

"Mother I don't feel good. Can I skip my bath and go to bed?"

"I don't give a shit, Sarah." That's all I needed to hear as I hurry to my room, put on my nightgown, kneel and fold my hands to talk to Jesus, then crawl into my bed. Derek walks into the bathroom to check on Curtis, passing me without a look or a word. Then I hear Curtis crying and Derek yelling. "Get washed up, you scumbag. Don't just sit there."

Then, I hear a lot of water splashing—Derek's probably dumping water over Curtis's head. He knows Curtis hates water in his eyes.

Wait. What if Derek *isn't* dumping water over his head but hurting him like he hurts me? Curtis has boy private parts, so maybe Derek can't do to him what he does to me. But what if he knows another way to hurt my little brother?

I squeeze my eyes shut and start to sing "Jesus Loves Me," but I stop in the middle of the song. There is no way I can lay here and not help Curtis, no matter what happens to me.

I look through a crack in the door and, yup, it's just like I thought—Derek's dumping water over Curtis's head, and it's getting into his eyes. Then Derek throws Curtis a washcloth. "Wash your own damn body because I'm not going to do it."

I climb back onto my bed and pull the blanket over my head—I don't want Derek to think I'm awake.

Derek walks through our room, one footstep, two, three—

Wait. Where's the fourth? The fifth? It takes more than three footsteps to get out of our room. I peek out through one of the holes in my blanket. Derek has stopped right in front of our bunk beds.

I do *not* move. I don't even breathe. I just close my eyes so Derek can't see me watching him.

He only stands there for a few seconds, which feels like hours to me.

Then, finally, he walks back into the bathroom.

I slit open an eye. Why is he doing this? Is he trying to scare me?

Curtis comes into our room in his underwear and grabs his ScoobyDoo pajamas.

Derek comes out of the bathroom a minute later, knocking into Curtis, who falls onto the bed.

Thank goodness he heads into the living room.

I need to make sure Derek isn't hurting Curtis. So, once I know he's dressed, I lean down from my bunk and ask in a whisper, "Curtis, does Derek hurt your private area?" The room is pretty dark, but I can see Curtis's big, gray-green eyes pop open after I ask the question, even in such little light.

He wrinkles his nose. "Ew, no."

"Does he touch you anywhere you don't like?"

"Yes."

Oh no. "Where, Curtis? *Where* does he touch you?"

"When he washes my hair, he scrubs it so hard and it hurts. I don't like it when he touches my hair."

"Is that it? Is that all, Curtis?"

He looks at me like I'm from outer space. "Yeah, that's it."

I let out a huge sigh. "Good."

183

"Tell me if he ever tries to do anything else, okay?" "Okay, Sarah," Curtis says slowly,

"Promise me Curtis," I hold out my pinky.

Curtis steps onto the wooden ledge of the bed I use to climb down from mine and wraps his pinky around mine, and we shake on it.

Now that I've dodged bath time with Derek, I need to get outside to hear Daddy play tonight. I don't want to miss it. Plus, I told him I would be there.

Mother puts Emma down for the night, and Curtis is in the living room watching *Gilligan's Island*. I can hear the silly song from my room because Curtis always listens to the television too loud.

"Curtis, turn that noise down. And after you watch *Gunsmoke*, you need to go to bed."

She definitely talks nicer to Curtis than she does to me. I've never seen her try to put his hands under hot water. Instead, she likes to put dish soap in Curtis's mouth when he does something she doesn't like, which seems better than what she does to me.

I don't hear Curtis's answer, but this is my chance to catch Mother before she goes out to the garage.

I hurry down off my bunk, fling open the door to my bedroom, and shout, "Mother, wait!"

"What, Sarah? What's your problem now?"

"My stomach's all better. Can I get dressed and come outside to listen to Daddy's band for a while? Please, Mother? He'll wonder why I'm not there."

"Fine, but you're not stayin' out there all night, ya hear me?"

Daddy's deep voice echoes from under the garage door. Derek turns to look at me as I walk in, and I swallow hard. Daddy looks at Derek and frowns. Did Derek tell him about me being dirty? But then Daddy looks right at me, and his entire face lights up, and I wave at him.

"I want to dedicate this next song to my little musical mascot." He waves at me and winks.

I, of course, try to wink back and close both eyes.

People laugh a little when they see me try it, but I don't mind because it reminded me of church when we laughed at Debbie's Kool Aid ring around her lips.

Still, I don't like all these people staring at me and want to run out of the garage, but then Daddy's voice comes out of the speakers again, so I stay put.

"She's the best little dancer this side of Carl's Creek, Ohio. Ready to show them how you dance, Dolly?"

I put my shoulders back and stand a little taller. The band starts playing "The Twist" by Chubby Checker. Daddy's singing and I want to dance. I do. I love to do the twist in the garage when it's just Daddy and me. I shimmy down to the floor and up again over and over.

But Derek is watching me now.

I look at Derek. I can't do it.

Daddy looks at me and then at Derek, and he frowns again.

I wish Derek wasn't here.

I start to dance and twist. I stop looking at Derek and focus on Daddy like he's the only one in the room. I forget about everyone else. It's only Daddy and me in the garage listening to our music and dancing together like we always do.

No matter what anyone does to me, especially Derek, they can never take away my favorite things: playing in the creek at the sluice pipe fort, helping Daddy in the garage, going to church, listening to music, and dancing.

Chapter 25
Hood Ornament & Foster Kid

Daddy told me a jaguar is a huge, wild cat.
I love cats and ask if I could have the metal cat on the car's hood.
He asked Frank, his friend who owns the junkyard, to use his torch
to take the hood ornament off for me.
I put it in the hole in my mattress. I thought I'd have to wait
until spring to take it to our sluice pipe and put it
with the rest of our treasures down there.
After Daddy gave me the hood ornament, I told him,
"Someday, I will have a Mustang and a Jaguar, and we can both
paint stripes on them together."

Monday morning finally gets here. Yay, all my brothers are gone because they went hunting and left early. But, like always, Daddy is in the garage working.

"Ow," Curtis is wrestling on the porch with his boot. It won't go on his foot.

"Come on Curtis, let's go. I'm sick of hearin' ya whine about your toes." Mother gets her coat on and gets Emma bundled up while Curtis slides his feet into his sneakers, leaving his heels out.

"It's bad enough wastin' my money on one pair for ya, but two pairs? Humpf, that's just too much damn money," she keeps saying repeatedly like a broken record.

"Can I go too?" "What for? Ya don't need new boots. Yours fit fine. I don't need ya to tag along," she snaps, and then the door closes, leaving me alone.

After everyone leaves, it sounds so quiet in the house. I can watch whatever and sit wherever I want. After moving the metal rabbit ears on top of the TV and turning the knob, I find Bugs Bunny.

Food. Oh my gosh. I can eat whatever I want because Mother isn't here.

I look out the window to make sure no one's coming to the house. Nope. Home free.

I creep into our kitchen, pull the stool out of the closet, stand on it and grab a slice of bread from the bag on top of the fridge. I swear Mother keeps it up here so I can't reach it. She probably thinks I'll sneak bread in the middle of the night… which I actually might.

I put the bread in the toaster and get out the butter. I can put as much on it as I want, and I do. It's sooooo good. Maybe I'll get just one more slice—

What if Mother *counts* the pieces of bread? She might think she counted wrong with one slice gone but not two.

Which stinks because I'm hungry right now; it is usually hard for me to eat because my stomach always hurts—and it's a thousand times worse when Derek's with us for dinner. I feel like I'm going to throw up the whole time we're eating, and Daddy always asks me if I'm okay. Derek glares at me, so I always say, "I'm okay. My stomach is upset. That's all." His eyebrows go up when I give my answer, but nothing more is said.

What else can I say? It's not like anything will stop all these things from happening to me. Besides my stomach hurting, I feel nothing.

I feel like my whole body is asleep but without tingling.

After eating my slice of toast, I clean up all the crumbs, so no one knows what I did, then I go back to the living room to watch more television.

And then the front door creaks open.

My head spins around quickly.

Derek is coming through the door, stepping into the living room.

I never heard his car pull in, and I didn't hear him coming up the porch steps. I liked being by myself so much that I missed all the sounds that tells me someone is coming. I'm always very good at listening for those noises because of how the boys treat Curtis and me. I make sure I'm able to see who walks into a room, and that's why I always face the boys' bedroom instead of the living room when I'm on my bunk bed.

Ever since the night Derek gave me a bath and checked me, I'm like Mama Cat, who seems to be able to hear trouble coming from a mile away.

I've been even more careful, watching doors and listening for any sounds that might let me know someone is coming. But I thought I'd be alone most of the day.

The toast suddenly feels like rocks in my stomach, and my mouth gets dry.

Derek takes off his boots, throws them by the heater on the mat in the living room, then smiles, making the rocks in my stomach tumble over each other.

I'm so glad I didn't sneak another slice of toast because I'd probably barf it up at his *smell*. Plus, if he'd seen me eating it, telling Mother would be another threat he'd use against me.

He doesn't say a word, just turns off the television and points to his room.

Then… he locks the front door.

Is this really happening again?

I need to get out of here.

But Derek pushes me toward his room. "Move it, Sarah." I have no choice.

I can't believe this is happening.

And then we reach *my* room. "Hey, Sarah,"

Maybe… maybe he's *not* going to—

Splat!

I whirl around.

Derek smashed Billy with my horse book. "That's better."

He *knew* I cared about him. He knows I love animals, *any* animal. So, he killed Billy to hurt me. And he used my horse book from Mrs. Young to do it.

I want to cry for Billy because maybe it'll be enough to stop Derek from taking me to his room, but I'll *never* let Derek see me cry. Not when he makes me play The Book Game and beats me with his belt or makes me box with Curtis. Not when he tells Terry to shoot me with BBs. Not then, and *not* now. I can't stop them from hurting me, but I won't ever let them see me cry about it. Not if I can help it.

I am *so* angry.

He *has* to be lying about checking me. It *has* to be just another way for him to hurt me. But this is my life. If I can't fight him, if I can't leave, if I have to protect Curtis, if I don't want Daddy to leave, and if I can't tell, then this is how it is.

I turn toward the back of the house and walk into his room.

And then he does the same thing he always does to me.

I thought the dead animal on the road by the sluice pipe was the worst smell ever—well, next to Mother's dinners—but it's *nothing* compared to Derek right now. His feet, his body, his sweat... It's awful.

I hold my breath as long as possible, but I have to finally breathe. That's when I raise my head to see what's happening.

"Lie back, Sarah, and just look at the ceiling." He's out of breath but so, so angry.

Why is he angry at me? *I'm* not hurting *him*.

Derek tells me the difference between a boy and girl parts as easily as if he were telling me what we are having for supper.

I say nothing.

Instead, I stare at the poster of the smiling bathing suit lady. Why is she so happy?

Whatever Derek is doing today hurts worse than anything he has done so far. "Sarah, just lie still, it's just my finger."

Just his finger. He's doing something different with it. I want to scream but don't dare because he'll keep doing what he does to me anyway. No one's going to stop him. I thought nothing could be worse than that first time, but I'm wrong.

As I stare at the poster, black spots float around the room, and it spins really fast.

"Sing to me, sing to me," a voice tells me inside my head.

I don't even think about it; I just start to sing "Jesus Loves Me" in my mind over and over.

But I can *still* smell him.

I need to disappear from this.

I go back inside my head and sing.

Then it's over.

Derek is always coming up with more reasons why I can't tell anyone about what he does to me when no one is around.

"Don't even try to tell Dad like you were going to that day in the garage. I know what the hell you were going to do. Why do you think I was out there? If you tell, you'll be tossed out of this house faster than lightning by Mother because you, like your shit brother, are foster kids."

I can't think about what words Derek is saying. I just need to leave this room. As soon as I stand up, I begin to gag. "If you throw up in my bedroom, you'll lick it up. Now keep your mouth shut, or I'll beat the shit out of you two."

I've got to get out of this house.

Derek left the bedroom, but I have no idea where he went.

I put my clothes on as fast as I can. Even though I'm hurting, I run to the front door. I unlock it, and just before I run outside, I go back to my bedroom. I grab the jaguar metal piece Daddy said I could have from the hood of the car we saw during our junkyard trip together. I almost fall while climbing up to my bunk, getting the Jaguar out of the hole in my mattress. I'm hurrying to grab it before Derek comes out and finds me again.

I hear music playing back in Derek's room and hope he plans to stay back there for a while. But, even if he doesn't, who cares? Could he really do anything worse to me? I get down from my bunk with the Jaguar and shove it into my pants pocket.

I run to the kitchen and grab some grapes from the refrigerator. I don't even care if Mother sees that the grapes are gone. I'm tired of being hungry all the time, and she's not here to stop me.

I put the grapes inside a napkin and race outside to head down to the creek to hide until I have to go back to that house.

"Hey Dolly," Daddy yells from the garage, "can you come help me for a minute?"

I look at the house door to make sure Derek isn't coming.

He's not, so I head into the garage.

I try to catch my breath, but I'm hurting from what he did to me. I'm even walking funny. Hopefully, Daddy won't notice.

"What's the matter, Dolly?"

What's the matter, Dolly? What's the *matter?* How about *everything?* I just learned that if I tell you what Derek is doing, he will beat me. I think Derek is lying about me not being clean and just wants to scare me. What's *wrong?*

Everything!

And, I can say nothing!

"Nothing." I force a smile. "Do I need my safety gear, Daddy?"

"No, I just need you to hold this tape up by the hood."

I keep that smile on my face even if it kills me—because it'd kill me more if Daddy left.

"Are you sure you're okay, Dolly? You usually laugh and skip when I ask you to come into the garage to help me, but you're walking really slow and look like you're scared. Is everything okay?"

"I'm trying not to drop these grapes."

"Yes, you definitely don't want to drop your snack." He salutes me.

Boy, do I want to crawl under this car and hide because I've had to lie to him so many times lately.

Then, he puts his hand on my shoulder and squeezes it lightly. "You know you can tell me anything. You know that, right?" I nod and look away.

"Was it just you and Curtis up there in the house?"

"No. Mother took him to get new sneakers and boots. His were too small."

Daddy's eyes get bigger. "How are your shoes fitting you? Is that what's going on with you? Are your shoes too small?"

Ohhhhhh. Daddy thinks I'm walking slowly because my shoes don't fit.

I want to lie and tell him they are tight so he stops trying to figure out what's going on with me, but I can't keep lying to him.

I've gotten pretty good at this lying thing though.

Derek comes out of the house, the door banging behind him. He waves at Daddy and me, gets into his car, then leaves.

I slip behind Daddy's back.

Daddy waves. He turns. "Dolly, where are you? Are you all, right?" Now that Derek's leaving, I definitely am.

"Yes!" I shout.

He looks at Derek's car, then back at me, shakes his head, and says, "Let's get started."

"Can we put the radio on and sing, Daddy?" I don't want to think about Derek anymore. Especially in here. This is where I am happy.

"Of course, sweetheart." He puts Johnny Cash on and starts singing. He sounds just like him.

Daddy is walking toward me, now spinning the roll of tape on his wrist. I feel so much better now that Derek's gone and I'm out here helping Daddy.

I look at the car. "Cama, Camo, Cammar." He laughs, "Camaro, sweetie." "Oh, Camaro." Daddy's getting it ready for Vinnie. "What color should we paint this car?"

"Pink."

"I thought you said pink was a girl color?" He puts his finger on his chin.

"It is, but a lot of girls like Vinnie, so it should be pink."

Laughter fills the garage. "Oh, Dolly, that's such a good idea, but I think Vinnie might like another color better. Maybe we should paint his car red and have a Playboy Bunny hanging from the rearview mirror."

"Ooh, I *love* bunnies. Could I get one, too?"

He shakes his head. "No, Dolly. This bunny is for boys."

My shoulders drop. "How come boys get all the good stuff?"

"Don't worry. When it's your turn to get a car, we'll make it exactly the way you want it—colors, stripes, animals, and all!"

"What are you going to do now, Dolly?"

I head to the workbench. "I'm going to the creek to hide this before someone takes it," I hold up the jaguar statue.

"Sounds like fun. Off you go!"

"Bye, Daddy! See you soon!" Running at full speed, then stopping quickly as the pain in my girl parts feels like I got shot there with the BB gun. Derek ruined my morning, and even when I try to forget about him and what he does to me, the pain in my private parts reminds me. It's like he's with me everywhere I go. I can't get away without smelling him or feeling what he does to me. One hand is in a fist smashing my grapes, and the other is gripping my Jaguar so tight it leaves marks on my hands that stay there even after I hide it under the L-shaped rock.

Curtis arrives, and I spin around, holding the garter snake by the tail, the body has wrapped around a stick. "Sarah, how do you know that's not a rattlesnake?" I point to the snake's head and show him this one is round and tell him rattlesnakes have a triangle shaped head. Plus, I show him the colors are different than a rattlesnake. "If this was a rattlesnake, it would be making noise." "Yuck Sarah, why do you like to catch snakes? Gross." "Because I do," I tell him while putting the snake back down in the grass. Finally, I look at Curtis's feet. "Why are you wearing your old shoes?"

"Mother said I couldn't wear my new shoes and boots 'cause I'd mess them up." His big toe is sticking out of the front of one shoe. "Maybe Daddy has a tool we could use to cut the top so your toes won't be jammed inside. Come on."

We start up toward the house even though Mother hasn't called us yet. Daddy is already inside, so I decide to wait until tomorrow to ask him to help us with Curtis's shoe.

The other boys are home, but Derek isn't there. We can hear Mother and Daddy in the back bedroom arguing when we walk in. But Terry has to say something mean as always. "Hey, alien. Hey, Bucky. Where have you two been, and why did you come back?" Vinnie and Terry laugh.

"Shut up," I say.

I'm angrier than I used to be and can't take the name-calling and keep my mouth shut anymore. Of course, it helps that they won't hurt me with Daddy in the house. But now I don't stop even if Daddy's not here.

Terry stands up and walks toward me. "That's it, brat, I am going to punch you in your face." We all hear Mother and Daddy walking toward us, fighting, and it seems to stops Terry in his tracks.

Mother rolls her eyes when she sees Curtis and me standing there as she makes her way to the kitchen to start dinner, but Daddy cheerfully says hello. Mother and Daddy have been fighting a lot more lately. It can't be about me this time. I have been very careful to hide my bruises and blisters around Daddy.

"I can smell you two from here," she shouts from the kitchen.

How can she smell us over the smell of the boys' boots by the heater and the scent of whatever she's started cooking up in the kitchen?

I begin to look around. First the living room, then the kitchen. Finally, I peek outside to look for Derek's car and let out a deep breath.

Daddy comes up behind me and puts his hand on my shoulder.

"Whatcha looking for, Dolly?"

"Is Derek here?"

"No, he won't be coming back tonight."

When I hear that good news, I release my fists.

"Sarah, git in the tub first. I'll be in to start your water for you. Can ya handle washin' your hair tonight or do I need to make sure ya do it right?" She shouts out to me from the kitchen.

"I can do it." Oh, I'm *definitely* doing it myself. No one is ever going to wash me or my hair. Well, unless… "You don't need to wash my body, do you, Mother?"

She doesn't answer. Instead, Mother walks out to the living room, looking from me to Daddy as we stand by the picture window.

"No, Sarah. You're old enough to do it yourself. Besides, ya do a good job washin' your body, unlike your brother. It's just your hair that ya don't wash good enough."

I knew it. I knew it. Derek is a liar!

After bath time, I get to the table and see a stinky meat, worse than venison, on everyone's plates. No way I'm going to eat this stuff. "Mother, I'm not hungry."

Mother drops her fork onto her plate. "If ya get down from this table, young lady, you're gettin' nothin' else to eat tonight. Do ya hear me?"

"Come on, Donna." Daddy taps Mother's hand. "I agree the kids need to eat what you put in front of them, but even I had a tough time with liver and onions when I was a kid."

Mother yanks her hand from under Daddy's. "Stop babyin' her,

Joseph." She drags my plate away from me. "Off to bed with ya then." Fine by me. That stuff is gross.

I go to my room. I didn't even get lunch today, and now no dinner? I'm glad I stole the bread and grapes. I ate the grapes even though they were smashed.

I kneel to talk to Jesus.

"Dear Jesus, today stared out pretty good being by myself, eating some toast and watching TV until Derek came home and, well, you saw what happened because you see everything. It's not nice to want people to get hurt and I'm not praying for anything bad to happen to anyone. But *Please make Derek get away from me. I just want him to go away and leave me alone.*

The rest of the day and night was so much better without him here and with Daddy in the house. If you could make Derek move out like Travis that would be great because we never see or hear from him. Even if he moved out like Christy it would be better than nothing. I'm sorry to bug you about this problem Jesus, I'm sure you are busy with everyone talking to you, but I don't know who else to talk to about it. Amen."

My mind is racing, constantly spinning around thoughts of Mother, Derek, Curtis, my other brothers, the fort, school, Daddy, the cats, and food. It never stops; that's why school is so hard for me and why I can't sleep now.

I fall asleep for a while, but I wake up because my belly hurts so much from being hungry, and now I have to go to the bathroom. As I climb back up into my bed, I notice something sitting on it. What in the world? A plate. And on it, my favorite, a peanut butter, and jelly sandwich.

Only Daddy would do this for me. Only Daddy \

Chapter 26
Sweet Dreams & Looking Pretty

"Hey, Sarah." Sharon taps me on the shoulder.
Oh, great. Here it comes.
Sharon was nice to me today when I fell asleep,
but she's probably going to say something about me peeing myself.
I turn around very slowly.
She looks at me and smiles for the second time today.
"I like your skirt. You look very pretty."

I fall asleep at my desk in school the next day.

After feeling a little nudge on my shoulder, I open my eyes to see Mrs. Young sitting next to me on a small chair. "Sarah, you've been falling asleep a lot lately. Are you sleeping at home at night? Do you have a bedtime?" I look around the classroom and see it is empty. "Where are all the kids?" "The bell rang for recess, but you slept through it. So, I sent them out with Mr. Marks's class so I could spend some time with you."

"Yes, 8:30. I go to bed at 8:30." "Are you sleeping okay?" I shrug.

"Sarah, I need you to tell me. I'm going to have to call home if this behavior continues."

That's the *last* thing I want. Mother will *kill* me. I sit up straight in my chair and blink a lot. "I'm awake. I'm awake. I'm awake."

Mrs. Young pats the desk. "Okay, okay, settle down. Do you drink a lot of sugary drinks before you go to bed? They can keep you awake."

Inside my head, I tell Jesus I'm sorry for the lie I'm going to tell.

"Yep, I drink lots of them, Mrs. Young. That's what's wrong with me." "If you promise to stop drinking those drinks so you can get on a better sleep schedule at home and stay awake here at school, I won't need to call home about it. Deal?"

"Oh, yes, Mrs. Young. I won't have sugary drinks before bed." I cross my fingers under my desk.

Mrs. Young raises her eyebrows but walks away without another word. Just then, All the kids start coming back into the classroom. Robby sticks his tongue out at me as he walks by my desk.

I hate that kid.

After lunch, I'm tired again. I kick my feet under my desk and play with my fingers, but nothing helps me stay awake. Daddy says school is important, but I'm tired and don't like math. Mrs. Young calls what we're doing story problems. I like stories, but these stories have math in it, and that takes all the fun out of them.

On the chalkboard, she reads, "Jim is going fishing, and he brought 9 worms with him. He needs to catch 5 fish to have enough for his dinner. If he lost 2 of his worms and has 4 of them left, how many fish has he caught so far?"

How many…

Stop, Mother. Let go of my hair. I don't want you to cut my bangs again. The tugging on my hair isn't hard, but it bothers me—

I open my eyes. *Oh no.* I'm not at home. I'm at school and Mother isn't here.

I feel a tap on my back, and I turn around in my chair. The girl behind me is Sharon. She's beautiful and never talks to me, but right now, she smiles and whispers, "Sorry I was pulling your hair, but I was trying to wake you so Mrs. Young wouldn't catch you again." "Thanks," I whisper and turn back around.

Mrs. Young is now going around the room asking kids for answers to the story problems that she showed us how to do when I conked out. I'm using my fingers like I do when I add numbers, but I don't think it's working for these story problems since I keep getting the answers wrong.

And then, I have another problem.

A really, really big problem.

I have to go to the bathroom. Like, *now.* Lately, I've had to pee all the time, and when I have to go, I *have* to go! I can't hold it like I used to, but I don't want to get in trouble because I've used the bathroom thing as a way to get out of doing math. Mrs. Young figured it out and wasn't happy with me, so I'm trying to hold it now. Plus, it burns when I pee, and that's not nice. But, now, I *really* have to go. I can't hold it.

I squirm and raise my hand.

Mrs. Young smiles. "Sarah, what did you come up with for an answer?"

I squirm. "Um, I don't know, Mrs. Young, but I really have to go to the bathroom."

Her mouth tightens. "Sarah, honey, can you wait until math is over?" I shake my head.

She sighs. "Go ahead, Sarah."

I stand up—oh no! I waited too long! The pee pours out of me.

I turn into the hall while my pee keeps going down my legs.

The kids' laughter echoes after me. "Sarah peed her pants! Sarah peed her pants!"

I run into the bathroom and into one of the stalls. My white pants are *soaked*. So are my socks, shoes and underwear.

Oh no. I smell like pee. It's awful.

I take off everything on the bottom except my undies. As I start to peel those down, the bathroom door opens. *Is it Derek?*

No… it can't be. He never comes here.

I take a breath.

"Sarah, dear, are you okay?" Mrs. Young asks. "Uh-huh," I whisper. "Do you need help?"

What kind of help can Mrs. Young give me? I don't want anyone in here. I can't come out. I have nothing to wear.

"My pants, underwear, socks and shoes are soaking wet with pee," I finally say. I look at my underwear as I take them off. The toilet paper is still stuck in there from this morning. There are drops of blood, but they are more pink than red now. Not again. If I'm still bleeding, I need stitches for *sure*. Maybe I'm dying super-slow.

"Sarah," Mrs. Young says, "I'll call your mother and let her know you had an accident and that you need a change of clothes, okay?" "No!" Mother can*not* know.

It's quiet in the bathroom. Then, Mrs. Young asks, "How about I get you something to help you clean yourself up? I can also get you some new socks, shoes, and bottoms to wear."

"Okay." Phew. That was close. I don't want her to call Mother.

"Honey, can you check the tag on your pants and shoes and tell me your size?"

I look at my shoes and see a three on them, so I tell her my shoes are a three. Then I look at my pants for the tag but don't see one.

"Ummm…"

Mrs. Young sticks her hand under the door. "Hand me the pants." Ew. I don't want Mrs. Young to *touch* my pee-soaked clothes. "Nine," I tell Mrs. Young. "I need a nine." I'm nine years old, so that should make sense.

Mrs. Young pulls her hand away. "Are you sure, honey? That seems a little big. You're very tiny."

"Yes. I'm sure." I say so softly that I wonder if she heard me at first, but then I hear her shoes echoing off the cement floor as she turns to leave the bathroom.

"I'll be right back."

"Jesus loves me this I know," I sing.

My voice sounds so tiny in the big bathroom.

I close my eyes and fold my hands, hoping Jesus will be okay with me talking to him like this without kneeling. I don't think he would want me to kneel in the bathroom next to a toilet with no undies or pants on. "Jesus, can you help me today? I peed my pants and all the kids laughed at me. I don't want to go home. Mother will be so ticked off at me she'll probably give me three different punishments instead of one or two. I have no choice but to stay at school, so can you help the kids not laugh at me? Please? Thanks Jesus. Amen."

I keep my eyes closed after I talk to Jesus. I use my daydream of becoming a bird or horse to help me stop thinking about what happened and where I am right now.

Then, finally, I hear the *click, click, clack* sounds of Mrs. Young's shoes.

"Sarah, are you still in here?" she asks after she comes in.

"I'm still here, Mrs. Young. It's bad enough everyone saw me pee my pants. I don't think walking out with no bottoms on would make them stop making fun of me, so I'm still in here."

Mrs. Young laughs out loud, then clears her throat. "Don't worry. I'll deal with the kids. You can use these." She hands me some wet napkins under the stall door. They look like what Mother uses on Emma when she changes her diaper.

I use them to wipe the pee away.

"Here. You can wear these." She passes me a pair of low yellow socks, slip-on white sneakers, a pair of shorts, and a yellow skirt.

"A skirt?" I say out loud, a little too sassily, to someone who's being so nice to me. I never wore one of those before.

"Yes, Sarah, I'm sorry. It's the only piece of clothing I could find that would fit you. The size-nine clothes looked too big. We usually have underwear on hand, but we don't have any left that would fit you, so I brought shorts for you to wear under it."

Good thing we already had recess today.

I hear Mrs. Young's voice, "Sarah, I can call your mother instead, and she could bring you something from home if you don't like the skirt." "No! Don't call her!"

"Okay, okay. Calm down, honey." She hands me a big plastic bag. "Put your wet clothes in this, Sarah, and I'll get them cleaned for you."

As I put my clothing in the bag, a couple of girls open the door to the restroom.

Oh no. Please don't let those girls come in here. They'll make fun of me.

Mrs. Young reads my mind. "Girls, this restroom is closed. You'll have to use the lavatory in the nurse's office."

"Thank you, Mrs. Young." I can barely get the words out. She's being so nice to me.

"Oh, Sarah, it's okay, honey. What happened today?" "I don't know, Mrs. Young. I can't hold my pee anymore." Neither of us says anything for a bit.

Then Mrs. Young asks, "Sarah, is everything okay at home?"

If only I could tell Mrs. Young about Derek, maybe she could make him stop. I mean, if she can make an entire class stop picking on me about peeing myself, she can probably stop Derek.

But then everyone will know about me being dirty. And, if Derek's right, Mrs. Young might not like me or want to help me anymore if she knows. And if I tell, Derek said he'd hurt Curtis, and I can't let him do that. Plus, he said no one will believe me anyway. So, I guess Derek's right, and I need to stay quiet. "Yes, everything's fine." Mrs. Young. I quickly close my eyes and whisper, "Sorry, Jesus."

"Sarah, you take your time getting cleaned up and dressed, and you come back to the classroom when you're ready. I'm heading back there now."

"Okay, Mrs. Young." Wait. Go back when I'm *ready*? Maybe I won't be ready for the rest of the day. We still have to finish math, science, story-time, and then head home. I could hang out here instead of going back for those lessons. Besides, now I have to show up in class wearing this skirt. It's sort of pretty, but, like Daddy said, I'm a tomboy. I don't like girly clothing, and a skirt is girly. Oh, why did this happen to me?

I step into the stretchy black shorts Mrs. Young gave me, but I don't pull them up the whole way yet. First, I grab more toilet paper, wrap it around and around my hand, and then put it all in the middle on the inside of my shorts, then pull them up. When I reach up to get the skirt off the hook on the back of the door, the toilet paper falls out. These shorts are too loose on me. *Think, Sarah. How can you fix this problem?*

The girls had come into the bathroom right when I was going to hand the bag of wet clothes to Mrs. Young, so I forgot to give it to her. She must have forgotten about it, too. My wet underwear's in that bag. I'm going to have to put them back on to keep the toilet paper in place. Gross, but I don't have any other choice.

I look up and whisper, "Jesus, if you have a better idea, now would be the time to tell me." I wait and listen really hard, but all I can hear is the *drip, drip, drip* of one of the sinks in the bathroom. Darn.

I take out the underwear, then squeeze them over the toilet, trying to get the pee out. Then I swing them around, trying to dry my undies. I wipe them with toilet paper, but the paper falls apart. If only this bathroom had some spray or Old Spice it would help get rid of the pee smell in my underwear.

I take the shorts off and step into my cold, smelly underwear, making a face. I take the ball of toilet paper I made, put it in the middle of my panties, and pull them up. I slip the shorts on over my underwear and then put the yellow skirt on over the shorts. I put on the socks and shoes, though I'm still not ready to go out and face the class yet.

I come out of the stall and sit on the tile floor by the sink. Daddy says the boys can't go in the bathroom when I'm in there, but Mother told Derek to help me wash my hair, and now he checks me to make sure I'm clean—or so he says—so I don't get in trouble with Mother. But how can Derek be allowed in the bathroom when Daddy says no boys are allowed—unless...

Mother's the one who told Derek to wash my hair, and *Mother's* the one who will punish me if I'm not clean enough. Maybe… maybe what's happening with Derek is another way Mother is punishing me. "Sarah, Sarah it's time to come back to class. Sarah?" I open my eyes. Mrs. Young is back in the bathroom.

"You need to come back to class now, Sarah. I promise you it will be okay."

I rub my eyes, trying to wake up the rest of the way.

"Sarah, I need you to be honest with me about why you keep falling asleep in class." Before I can answer, she asks, "Are you sleeping okay at home?"

I thought I'd fooled her with my answer about sugary drinks earlier, but I guess not. I'm not sleeping much at home—I wake up at every little sound and have a hard time falling back to sleep. Even though I *know* Derek won't touch me with Daddy in the house, I worry about him sneaking into my room to check on me.

"I sleep fine, Mrs. Young, except when I have those sugary drinks before bed like I told you before."

As I stand up and stretch, Mrs. Young says, "Oh, Sarah, you look so pretty in the skirt and matching socks."

I push my hair back and look at myself in the mirror. I do sort of look pretty. But then my hair pops out from behind my ears, and my bangs fall in my eyes again.

"Can I brush your hair and put it in a ponytail?"

"You mean tie it up?"

"Yes. I think it will look pretty with your skirt, and it will help you see better."

I nod, and Mrs. Young shows me the brush and a black hair tie.

While she's brushing my hair, I tell her about the metal slides Miss Sandy gave me to use and how Daddy's going to make me some out of scrap metal in his garage.

"There." She finishes. "Want to see your hair?".

I take in a deep breath and look. I freeze. Is that *me*?

My ponytail looks pretty with curls coming out of it, and my unibrow doesn't look so bad after all. But I still hate it. "I… I'd like my bangs over my big eyebrow, Mrs. Young."

"Sarah, I promise, you look very nice. Let's go back to the classroom." She holds out her hand.

After everything she's done for me, I'd like to hold *her* hand.

When I get to the classroom, I keep my eyes down but peek up now and then to see if anyone is looking at me.

A lot of kids are, but no one says a word. Robby is smirking like he wants to say something, but he stays quiet.

I get to my seat. Oh, thank goodness it's been cleaned up.

"Class instead of reading a book during story-time today, we'll go around the room and share stories about a time when we did something embarrassing at school." She isn't even finished talking before kids in the class raise their hands to tell their stories. Some are funny, but we only laugh if they laugh about it as they tell us.

One girl, Julie tells a story about getting on the wrong bus and how the other kids made fun of her while the bus driver yelled at her. Julie almost cries while telling her story. No one laughs, and Mrs. Young hugs her. "I'm sorry that happened to you." It seems to make Julie feel better. Hugs do help you feel better, just like when Daddy hugs me.

Once we're done telling our stories, Mrs. Young walks up and down the aisles between our seats, passing out our graded spelling tests. As Mrs. Young gets closer to my desk, I put my head down, knowing the four-letter word that will be written on top of my paper.

Mrs. Young stops at my desk. "Good job, Sarah. You've been working hard. I can tell." She sets the spelling test on my desk.

"GOOD" is written across the top of the paper in bright red ink. And that's not all. A sticker in the shape of a star—all gold and shiny—is next to it. I can hardly wait to show Daddy.

"Hey, Sarah." Sharon taps me on the shoulder. *Oh, great. Here it comes.* Sharon was nice to me today when I fell asleep, but she's probably going to say something about me peeing myself.

I turn around very slowly.

She looks at me and smiles for the second time today.

"I like your skirt. You look very pretty."

I don't know what to say, so I just say, "Thanks."

When we get our coats to leave, a girl named Marlo, who's friends with all the pretty girls, walks up to me and stares. I try to ignore her because I don't want to look at her if she is going to make fun of me.

"Hey, Sarah."

Ugh. I have to look at Marlo.

Dr. Sharon Zaffarese-Dippold
Melissa Mulhollan

She smiles and motions for me to come closer.

I really don't want to do this.

But I do.

She puts a hand around my ear and leans in. "Sarah, guess what?" she whispers, "I peed my pants in first grade one time. It was awful." She pats me on the back and then gets her coat and boots.

Wow. A girl who is pretty and smart and has lots of friends, had the same thing happen to her.

I guess it can happen to anyone.

Chapter 27
It's Derek & Cold

Even though the garage is toasty warm from Daddy's coal stove,
my teeth are chattering.
Daddy sits on his wheelie stool and puts me on his knee.
"Dolly, honey, what's wrong? Are you cold? You're shaking."

I am not used to walking around in skirts, and it's tough to get off the bus. Plus, I'm super-cold and have goosebumps the whole way up my legs. But Sharon saying I look pretty warms me up. Funny how my day started off so bad, but then things flipped around. And now I get to show Daddy my spelling test!

Daddy's taping up a shiny black Cadillac, another of my favorite cars, and— *Oh. No.*

How did I miss Derek's car in the driveway, and what is he doing in here with Daddy?

"Hiya, Dolly." Daddy waves at me. "Look at you in that pretty skirt and with your hair up. You look as pretty as a postcard. Come on over here and let me see you." I'm frozen like a popsicle.

I can't move at all.

And, as I realize Daddy's talking, I can't hear either. His mouth is moving, but I don't hear anything.

I have to move.

Daddy waves me over.

Come on, Sarah. Make your legs move. Derek can't hurt you with Daddy here.

I try. I really do. But nothing happens.

Come on, Sarah, move your legs. Move your legs.

I can't. I just… can't.

205

"Dolly?"

But at least I can hear Daddy now.

"Honey, come inside and close that door. It's cold out there." *Come on! Move!*

My body isn't listening to what my mind tells it to do.

And then it—*I*—start shaking.

"Sarah?" Daddy's serious when he uses my real name. "Come over here, please. I would like to see you. What do you have in your hand?"

I'm stuck between the outside and the garage door. It's like the cement floor in the garage is quicksand, and if I step inside, it'll swallow me up, and I'll be gone forever.

But then I'll miss Daddy and so many other people, places, and things.

I finally manage to take a breath, and then I can feel my legs again. I take one step inside.

I close the garage door—and, phew! I *don't* sink into the floor and disappear.

I'm almost sad that I don't…

"Sarah?"

I walk very slowly toward Daddy. All I can smell is Derek's sweat and stinky feet—the smell of Old Spice and paint that I always love when I walk into Daddy's garage now smells like… *Derek.*

And there he is, right next to that beautiful Cadillac.

Next to my daddy.

Even though the garage is toasty warm from Daddy's coal stove, my teeth are chattering.

Daddy sits on his wheelie stool and puts me on his knee. "Dolly, honey, what's wrong? You must be cold. You're shaking."

"She has a skirt on, and her coat is hanging open and it's the dead of winter; it's no wonder she's shaking." Derek has that awful smirk on his face that I want to just smack off of him.

But then he'd hurt me.

Of course, I don't know how he could ever hurt me more than he does—

Oh, no! He's seen me in my skirt.

That's why he's smirking.

I stop breathing. I need to throw up.

That's when the hiccups start.

Jesus, can't today go back to being good again?

My hiccups get louder, and I can't stop, so I bury my face in Daddy's shoulder, hoping he'll make them—and Derek—go away.

Daddy lifts my head and looks at me.

Which makes me see Derek behind him. *I am* not *going to get a bath tonight. I won't, and no one can make me.*

Daddy pats my back and looks from me to Derek. "Dolly, why don't you go inside and ask Mother to give you a spoonful of sugar and some water to help you get rid of those hiccups while I talk to your brother here?"

I almost forget I have the hiccups. Between them, I shake my head and beg, "Please don't make me go inside. I need to stay with you."

"I promise you'll be okay inside the house. Now go inside for me, okay? Do it for me?" He pats my back again.

"Will... will you come inside the house early tonight, Daddy? Please? *Before* I have to get a bath." If he says no, I will not take a bath tonight or *ever* again unless he's in the house. *Ever.*

Daddy tilts his head. "Sure, Sarah. Please don't worry."

I nod, slide off Daddy's lap, then walk backward out of the garage, tugging my skirt down my legs, watching Derek the whole way out.

I run up the porch steps, put my boots in the bin, then rush into the house. Mother's in the kitchen, and Curtis's in the living room hanging upside down on the couch, talking to himself. I don't see Emma or the other boys, thankfully.

I go into the kitchen, still hiccupping. Mother doesn't even look at me. Good. I don't want her to see my new clothes. I don't want to get in trouble again.

I sit at my seat to hide the bottom part of what I'm wearing and stare at the door. *Please don't let Derek come in without Daddy.*

"Sarah, why the hell are ya sittin' at the table? Get away from it. It's not time to eat." She's pouring herself pop while looking at a magazine, smoking away.

"Daddy told me to tell you that I need some sugar and water to get rid of my hiccups."

"Ya can have water 'cause sugar will spoil your supper." She doesn't even look up from the magazine as she gets my water from the sink and sets it on the table.

I don't know how I'm supposed to drink the water with hiccups. It'll come right back up.

But the hiccups are getting louder, so I reach for the cup.

My hands are shaking so much that I almost spill the water, which would get me in *more* trouble.

Calm down and drink. I take a big gulp and then set it back down. Maybe if I just sit here for a second, my hands—and the rest of me—will stop shaking.

A car starts up. I fold my hands and close my eyes. *Please let it be Derek's. Please let him be leaving. For* good!

Mother finally looks up from her magazine and heads to the living room window. "Is that Derek leavin' already? Well, that's strange. I thought he said he was stayin' for supper tonight."

I don't know who she's asking because it's not me. But I don't care. Derek isn't going to be here!

I look up at the ceiling and whisper, "That was fast." And just like that, my hiccups are gone. Just like Derek.

I decide to get up from the table and head to my room to change my skirt into something warmer. Then, I'll go back out and show Daddy my spelling test. I have to use the bathroom, so I head over there, sliding the bathroom door shut and waiting for a second. Once I'm sure I don't hear any sign Derek has come back into the house, I pull down my panties to sit on the toilet. I smell something gross and realize it's my underwear. It's dry now but smells like a skunk. I look at the toilet paper in my gross undies. At least there's no new blood on it. I still have a burning feeling from my girl parts as I pee.

I go into my bedroom quietly and open the plastic drawer to get new undies, pants and a shirt. Before I take off my clothes to change, I listen at my door for a few minutes again, double-checking to make sure Derek isn't back. Once I decide it's safe, I put on my pants and a sweatshirt. I take my new clothes and shove them into my backpack until I find another place to keep them. I keep the bag of pee-soaked clothes in my bag from school, too, until I can figure out how to get them in the laundry without Mother seeing so I don't get in trouble. My used underwear is almost dry but still smelly. I shove the panties under Curtis's bed as far back as possible so no one will find them.

I grab my crumpled spelling test and head out to see Daddy. As I get close to the door, Mother yells, "Sarah, make sure ya put those clothes from school in the hamper so I can wash 'um and git 'um back to your teacher, ya hear?"

What? Mother knew I had different clothes on this whole time, and she said nothing? I can*not* believe she isn't mad. She's screamed at me for a lot less. But instead of asking Mother any of these questions, I just shout "Okay!" on my way out the door.

I put my boots on at the top of the porch, making sure Derek's car isn't there. Then, when I'm sure he's gone, I race down the steps and back to the garage.

I peek inside.

No Derek.

Phew.

I go in the garage, doing a little skip but not pushing my luck with my girl parts being sore. I'm now smiling and ready to show Daddy my test.

Daddy's not using any dangerous tools, so I'm good to go in wearing my snow boots. He looks at me and says, "Well, that's much better, Dolly. You seem much happier now." He sits down on his wheelie stool again, and I fling myself in his arms. "Oh, there's my girl. Your hiccups are gone and you aren't shaking. Did you get warmed up? Did Mother give you some sugar and water?"

"Yes, I'm all better, Daddy, but Mother gave me just water, no sugar."

"Where did you get that pretty little skirt, and where is it now?"

"I got it at school. I had an accident." I tell him the whole story— oh, I forgot to take out my ponytail. I reach up to take it down.

"Why are you doing that, honey? It looks pretty." "I don't want Mother to get mad at me." His smile goes away.

"Look, Daddy!" I hold out my test. "Look what I got on my spelling test."

"I knew you could do it, sweetheart." He hugs me. "You're such a good girl."

Am I? Will he still think so if I tell him what Derek does to me? I really don't want Daddy to be mad at me.

"Dolly, look at me, honey. I have something very important I need to ask you and I need you to tell me the truth, no matter what, okay? You have to promise me you will."

209

I've never heard Daddy sound so serious.

Oh no. Did Derek tell Daddy?

A tear slides down my cheek.

"Dolly… are you afraid of Derek?"

The hiccups come back. "I… I don't want to get in trouble with Mother, Daddy."

"Dolly, honey I cannot help you if you don't tell me. I know you're afraid of Mother, but maybe I can help you."

I take a deep breath and nod, but it doesn't stop my tears or hiccups.

Daddy just rubs my back, waiting for me.

"Daddy…" I hiccup. "Derek… he… he hurts my… girl parts."

Daddy's hand stops, and he takes a deep breath.

And then, a car pulls into the driveway.

The car door opens and then slams shut. Hard.

I need to know if it's Derek, but I don't want to look.

"Dammit!" *It's Derek.*

He stomps up the porch steps then slams the front door.

Daddy's quiet.

Too quiet.

Does he think I'm lying like Derek said would happen if I told anyone?

Daddy's just staring at the garage door without blinking.

And then I see a tear sliding down his cheek.

That's all it takes for me to cry harder.

"Sarah, I need you to run into the house and go to your room."

"What about Curtis, Daddy?"

His face goes white. "Does he hurt Curtis, too?"

"No. I asked Curtis, and he said no. But Derek told me he *would* hurt Curtis if I told anyone, and if you say anything to Derek, he'll know I told and hurt Curtis—oh, no. What about Mother? She'll be mad at me, too." I'm out of breath when I finish.

Daddy's just sitting there, not saying anything. Not even looking at me.

What have I done? Derek warned me not to say anything.

Then he clears his throat. "Grab Curtis if you see him and take him to your room with you. If you don't see him, go straight to your room, and scream if Derek tries to come anywhere near you. If Derek's in the bathroom, you come back out here when you go inside. If he's in his room, you go to my bedroom and wait in there. Don't come out until I tell you to. No matter what. Do you hear me, Sarah?" I nod. Because I can't talk.

Daddy hugs me and then wipes away his tears. He uses his hanky to dry my cheeks. "Don't worry about any of these things anymore. I know I didn't keep Derek from hurting you before, but I will *not* let it happen again. And don't worry about Curtis or your mother. I'll protect him and take care of her."

"Okay, Daddy." I sniff so I don't start crying again.

"I'm so very sorry." He hugs me for a long time.

I snuggle against him, smelling his Old Spice and finally feeling like Derek will never be able to hurt me again.

When Daddy lets go of me, he looks mad. Very, *very* mad. I've only seen this look on his face a couple of times, like when he chased those boys who wanted to take me for a ride, and when one of his customers told him he'd painted their car wrong, and a few times with Mother.

"I'm sorry, Daddy." I shouldn't have told him.

He touches my chin. "Sarah, this is not your fault. Remember that."

"But you look mad."

"I am, but not at you. Never at you. Okay?"

"Okay, Daddy."

"Go on inside the house, and you and Curtis go to your room. I need to talk to your mother."

I nod, then head for the house. Derek's inside, but I'm not as scared anymore. Daddy *didn't* get mad at me, and he *did*, believe me, so Derek was wrong.

Mothers in the kitchen cooking dinner, and Emma is in the high chair slurping noodles. I smell spaghetti sauce.

Derek is sitting at the table talking with Mother. Neither one of them look over when I come through the door. Vinnie and Terry still aren't home.

I go over to Curtis, who's playing on the floor with Emma's blocks, and whisper that Daddy's coming inside and wants us to go to our room now.

Curtis looks at me with big eyes, his eyebrows up high. Careful not to knock over the block tower he made, he stands up and follows me to our room, then quietly slides the door closed.

We get into our beds, and even though I know Curtis can tell I'm upset, we don't say a word to each other. It's pretty quiet except for the sounds of Emma pounding on her tray whining. I can hear Mother moving around the kitchen as she and Derek whisper to one another.

A few minutes later, the door from outside opens with a loud *bang* and, all of a sudden, Mother's screaming.

"Joseph! What are you doin'? Don't *shoot* him! *Don't* shoot him! What the hell are ya doin', Joseph?"

Derek then starts screaming, "Don't shoot me! What the hell did I do?"

Emma's crying now. We hear Mother begging Daddy to put the gun down and get it out of Derek's face.

"You molested Sarah! You thought it was *okay* to touch her? She's a little girl!" Daddy growls like a bear.

"I didn't! I swear! She's a liar!" Derek sounds really scared.

Good.

My heart's pounding. What if Daddy believes him? What if Derek makes them think I'm lying?

I climb down from my bunk onto Curtis's bed. We move to the back corner of his bed, sitting together as close as we can, hugging each other. Someone runs out the front door onto the porch.

"Run, Derek!" Mother yells. "Git out of here before your father does somethin' he'll regret tomorrow. Git on out of here!"

Jesus loves me, this I know, for the Bible tells me so.

"Did you know what he was doing to her?" Daddy yells.

"I don't believe it. He wouldn't do that to her. Or to anyone!" she yells back at Daddy.

It's just like Derek said would happen. Mother doesn't believe me.

"How could this happen?" Daddy shouts. "Why would he ever *think* he could be in the bathroom with her? I always tell the boys that the bathroom is off-limits when Sarah is in there. It's her private time."

"I told him to help them run the bath water and make sure their hair got washed. I didn't tell him to go in there with them or bathe them or nothin.' My boy just wouldn't do such a thing. She's a *child*!"

"And there's *no* way that child is lying, Donna. He *hurt* her!" I've *never* heard Daddy this loud.

"That boy better *not* come back to this house anytime soon if he knows what's good for him. And *you* stay the hell away from her, too. I better not find out that either of you did anything more to that child! I don't care if you don't believe her because I *do*!" His voice echoes off the walls. "I need to get out of this house. I'm going to the garage." He slams the front door shut.

He's leaving me here with *Mother*?

"Joseph!"

We're alone with Mother. Will she listen to him and leave me alone or come after me for telling on Derek?

I wonder. I sit in the bottom bunk with Curtis, shivering for what feels like hours. No one comes to our room. There's no noise in the house after Daddy leaves, and Mother gets Emma quieted down. Vinnie and Terry aren't home yet either.

Curtis falls asleep, so I climb onto my bunk—*just* as the door slides open.

Now what? *Who* is coming in here?

I hold my breath and lie there, not moving a muscle.

Mother walks in and places a plate with a sandwich on each of our beds.

Wow. I didn't think I was even hungry until now.

I can't see her very well in the dark.

Maybe she feels bad for what happened with Derek and believes me after all.

Maybe Mother will finally be nice to me now, and things will be better.

Chapter 28
Garbage Bags

"What happened to eating noodles tonight? And where's Daddy?" Mother doesn't answer. She just turns on a lamp, then walks out.

"Eat your supper," she mumbles as she slides our door closed.

No one woke us for school today.

It's just like that morning we met Mrs. A.—when we learned about our birth mother and that Mother isn't really our mother.

I hope Derek's not really my brother.

And I hope he's never coming back.

I hope things are different now. I hope Mother's gonna be nice.

And I hope the kids at school are gonna be, too. It's funny, but today, I'd kinda like to go to school to see if Sharon will talk to me now and be my friend. And maybe after Mother washes the clothes, Mrs. Young will tell me to keep them. That would be nice, but I don't think I'm gonna wear the skirt again, even though Sharon said I looked pretty in it.

And I don't want to leave without seeing Daddy. I feel bad that he was so upset last night, but I feel better knowing he'll never let Derek hurt me again. He believed me and protected me from Mother, too.

Then Mother flings open our door. "Git up and git dressed before ya come out of your room."

Curtis sleeps through the whole thing, so I wake him up.

"What do you want, Sarah?" He rubs his eyes, then stretches his arms above his head.

"Mother wants us to get dressed before we come out to eat breakfast."

His eyes get wide, and he sits up so fast it's like he's on a spring.

"What's going on, Sarah?"

I shrug. "I don't know, but we should hurry up."

We both dress quickly, so Mother doesn't get ticked off at us. Then, when we come out of our room, Curtis heads straight for the kitchen.

I look out the front window in the living room. Derek's car's not here, and neither is Vinnie's. I don't know who came home last night and who left this morning. I heard nothing. That doesn't usually happen.

But Derek's not home and I hope he'll never come home again.

I cross my fingers, close my eyes, and make that wish.

I could ask Mother where he is, but that's probably not a good idea since she doesn't seem to be in a good mood.

I sigh. Maybe things *haven't* changed with her.

Oh well. As long as Derek doesn't hurt me anymore, I guess I can stand Mother being mean.

I see smoke from Daddy's coal furnace rising in the air. So, I was right, Daddy must be in the garage already.

"Sarah, git over here." Mother sounds the same as usual.

Our bowls are already on the table, and Mother has put the cereal and milk in them, leaving us with mush to eat. I hate when she does that.

Things definitely haven't changed.

I sit at the table at my usual seat and push the clumps of cereal around in my bowl.

Curtis does the same thing, pushing the mush around with his spoon and not eating it.

"Hurry up you two," Mother says. "Eat your cereal. Ya don't have time to sit there all mornin'."

We both put small bits of the cereal on our spoons and then into our mouths, chewing slowly when Mother comes to the table with a box of garbage bags. She pulls one out and lays it next to me, then pulls out a second one and places it on the table next to Curtis.

I wait for her to tell us to empty all the garbage cans into the bags and take the garbage out, but she doesn't say a word.

Mother then walks over to pour herself a cup of coffee, then lights up a cigarette.

I look from the bag to her and then back again, but I don't say anything.

Terry walks out of his room and heads toward the door to go to school. Before he leaves, he turns back and looks at me. "So long, Bucky!"

Mother bangs her coffee cup on the counter. "Terry, ya didn't need to say that to her. Ya sound too happy that she's leavin'." "That's because I am!" He slams the door behind him.

"What does that mean, Mother?" I ask her.

Mother just takes a long sip from her coffee and then sucks on her cigarette while staring out the kitchen window. She turns around and then blows out the smoke. "Your bowls are still half full. Hurry up. You're runnin' out of time for breakfast." She stabs her cigarette out. "Ya have ten minutes to finish eatin', and then whatever's left in your bowl will get thrown out, and you'll be hungry 'til ya eat lunch." Curtis stares down at his bowl—as usual.

I can't stand the silence and suspense any longer, "What are we doing with these garbage bags?"

"When you're done with your breakfast, brush your teeth and then put your toothbrush in there." I'm surprised Mother answers me for a change.

But I don't like the answer. "What? Daddy just gave us new toothbrushes last week. We don't have to throw them away yet."

Mother glares at me for a few seconds before answering. "Not only will your toothbrush go in the garbage bag, Sarah, so will all the clothes in your dresser."

Why would she want us to throw away our clothes? Is this some new kind of punishment? I don't know if it's because of last night and Daddy standing up for me, but I *have* to say something.

I stand up. "No, Mother. I'm not going to throw away my clothes. I didn't do anything wrong for you to make me throw them away." I stomp my foot.

"Ya talk like that to me again, young lady, and ya won't like what happens to ya!" Mother says with her teeth gritted like always.

I guess Daddy's warning to her last night has already worn off.

"Won't we miss the bus for school?"

The look Mother gets on her face makes her look like a statue. She's not smiling, not sad, not angry. Nothing. "You and Curtis ain't goin' to school today, Sarah."

I'm not? Well, *that's* great. It can mean only one thing—our birth mother and sister no longer have bugs, and we get to visit them today. That's why Terry said he was glad I was leaving. I bet Mrs. A. will be coming any minute now to take us to visit her.

216

I sit back down and eat the mushy cereal, and so does Curtis though he ends up wearing as much as he eats. We rinse our bowls and then race back to our bedroom with the garbage bags.

"Curtis, come sit with me. I can help you put your clothes in your bag while I do mine."

He sits on the dirty floor next to me. "Sarah, what are we going to wear if Mother makes us throw our clothes away?"

"I don't know, Curtis. You know she gets mad at us and does mean things all the time."

"When ya finish with your clothes, put your toys in there too!" Mother yells from the living room.

Curtis and I make funny faces at each other. "What toys?" we ask each other at the same time. Curtis has two plastic Army men from our brothers that he can throw in his bag. I have no toys at home to put in mine.

We carry our garbage bags into the living room. It's not hard; we don't have much to put inside.

I have to say; this punishment is the meanest one she's come up with so far.

"Drop the bags by the door then park it on the couch." Why's she having us sit here?

When we do, she picks up our bags and puts them on the porch.

"What's she doing?" Curtis whispers.

"I don't know," I answer.

Mother puts our sneakers in the garbage bags, too. What a wicked witch! She's throwing away our shoes.

At least she left the boots there.

"Sarah," Curtis's voice is shaky. "Why's she throwing away all our stuff? What did we do?"

"That's it." I grit my teeth. "I'm going to punch her in the face." Curtis laughs. So, I start laughing with him.

Mother walks back inside rubbing her arms. "Brrr, it's damn cold out there this mornin'." She waves in front of the picture window when a car crunches over the snow on the driveway.

Mrs. A. steps inside. "I see you packed up. That's good."

"They're all yours." Mother picks up Emma, who drops her book. It lands at my feet. "See ya later, Kate."

I watch her go and then smile at Mrs. A. really big. "Are you here to take us to visit our birth mother today?" Curtis and I are so excited, we're bouncing in our seats.

Mrs. A. looks so surprised I think she might tip over. Finally, she sits down in Daddy's chair. "No, Sarah. Didn't anyone tell you and your brother what we're doing today?"

Curtis and I stop bouncing. Something's... not right.

Curtis looks at the floor, and I shake my head no.

Mrs. A. blows out a big breath and rolls her eyes. "Sarah." She says my name the same way I talked to Lucky that day she almost died. "You and Curtis are being moved to live with another family."

What? What does that even mean? What other family? *This* is my family. I may not like them too much, but I belong here with Daddy—but wait. "Is Daddy coming with us?"

"No, Sarah. He's not your father. He's your foster father. You and Curtis are foster children, and you're going to a new foster home." *What?* All this time I thought he was my real daddy, and he's *not?*

I jump off the couch. "Don't you *ever* say that to me again! *Ever!*" I scream louder than I ever have in my life, and I run to the door and fling it open while Mrs. A. yells my name. I run outside in the freezing cold, wearing no coat, and not stopping to put on my boots. I just run straight for the garage.

"Daddy! Daddy!" I'm shouting so loud my head, and throat hurt.

I throw open the door to the garage and run straight to him. He turns from his workbench.

He's crying. And he must've been for a while because his eyes and nose are red, and his face is wet.

"Daddy!" I jump into his arms, and he squeezes me tighter than he ever has before—like he will never let me go.

"Oh, Dolly, honey, I'm so sorry. I'm just so sorry," he says over and over.

"Daddy, Mrs. A. says you're not my daddy and that Curtis and I have to go to a new foster family. She said we are foster kids. Derek told me that, too, but I didn't believe him. Daddy, please tell me she's wrong. Please, tell me, Daddy. Please!"

He's shaking his head with tears rolling down his cheeks, looking down at the cracked cement floor like I've done so many times before.

218

Finally, he looks up at me. "I may not be your real father, but I will always be your daddy, Sarah. But I didn't keep you safe. I need to make sure you're safe, and the best way is for you to live with another family."

"No, Daddy! No! Derek didn't do anything. I'm sorry, Daddy. I take it all back. Please don't make me go. I'll listen. I'll never forget and drag mud into the house ever again. I'll eat all of Mother's food. *All* of it. I won't ask for more toast. Just please, please, *please*, don't make me leave you!" I will *die* if he says I have to go.

Daddy sniffs a lot and wipes his tears away. "Dolly, come over here." He sits on his stool and then pulls something from his pocket. "Here." He hands me a one-dollar bill. "You keep this dollar, sweetheart, and use it to get some ice cream at your new home." I nod, unable to speak.

"What's our phone number, Dolly?"

When I'm finally able to talk, I tell him.

"Good girl. Now you say it every night before you go to sleep so you'll never forget it." He takes a long breath… "I need you to promise me that you'll come back to see me when you turn eighteen years old. Promise me, Dolly." He brushes some of my bangs off my forehead and tucks them back behind my ear. "I want to see your beautiful brown eyes one more time while you promise me. *Promise* me, Dolly."

All I can do is stand there and nod. Tears pour down my face.

He brushes them away, then leans close to my ear. "You will always be my little Dolly. I love you, honey."

Mrs. A. walks in and hands me my boots and coat. "Please put these on, Sarah."

Daddy helps me with them.

"Mr. Connor, there will be no easy way to do this, so we just have to do it." Mrs. A. tries to take my hand.

"Get away from me!" I throw myself at Daddy, hanging onto his neck. "Please, Daddy! Let me stay with you!"

"Mrs. Alexander, I've got her." He zips up my coat, takes my hand, and walks outside as the snow falls from the sky.

Curtis is already in the back seat of the car. Daddy opens the front passenger door of Mrs. A.'s ugly green car. "No, Daddy, I don't want to sit in the front seat with her."

He closes the front door and then opens the back one. "Curtis, do you have a hug for me?"

Curtis puts his head down.

"Okay, how about a high-five?"

Curtis looks up at him, eyes wide, and high-fives him.

Daddy smiles. "Thanks, bud. How about you scoot over to make room for Sarah?" Daddy sits me on the seat and then leans in. "Hey, look out for your sister." He looks at me. "And, Sarah, you look out for your brother. It's just the two of you now."

He moves back, but before he can stand up, I wrap my arms around his neck, refusing to let go. "Oh, please, Daddy. Please! Don't make me go!"

Daddy pries my fingers from around his neck, and Mrs. A. reaches back from the driver's seat and grabs my arm.

"No! I'm not gonna go!"

I'm holding on, Mrs. A. is grabbing me, and Daddy is undoing my fingers—and then Curtis starts crying.

"Sarah, Sarah stop, please stop. Please stay with me." His voice is so shaky and soft. "Please don't let her take me away all by myself."

No way can I let Curtis go without me. No way, even if that means I can't stay with Daddy.

I let go of Daddy's neck, and no sooner does my butt hit the seat than the car door closes and locks. Now I'm trapped inside the car, unable to open the door to say goodbye to Daddy.

Curtis wraps his arms around me, crying.

I wrap my arms around him, too.

I look at the house. No one's on the porch or in the window.

Mother hasn't even come out to say goodbye.

Mrs. A. starts the car and begins to pull away.

I look at Daddy through the window.

The tears are still streaming down his face.

Mrs. A. may have locked the door to the car, but I can open the window.

I let go of Curtis and roll down the window as the car heads down the driveway.

"Daddy! You said I could stay with you forever! You promised!"

He shakes his head, puts his face in his hands, and his shoulders start shaking.

I look at the old, broken-down cars that line the driveway. Then I look at the garage where I'd spent hours and hours with Daddy— painting, singing, talking, laughing. I see the side of the garage where I'd built my forts and mud pie oven. I see the cars where I'd made homes for Mama Cat, Lucky, and her other kitties. I see the weeping willow, my yellow nightcrawler stand, and the place where I'd stood to catch the blue bus to church. Straight ahead now is Mr. Bob's farm and the goats we'd named Bertha and Larry where I got the hay for Mama Cat and the kittens.

As we reach the end of the driveway, I look down the road where the neighborhood boys live. Remembering our football games, spitting matches, and tree-climbing contests, where I first learned I was a girl.

We pull out and turn in that same direction. I remember walking up this road with my nightcrawlers and running home to Daddy when those boys chased me.

I see the creek—*our* creek—up ahead. I feel the sluice pipe beneath us as we drive over the bridge. Soon it will all be out of sight. Gone forever.

Goodbye, sluice fort. Goodbye, treasures under our L-shaped rock. Goodbye, Mama Cat and Lucky. Goodbye, cars. Goodbye, garage. Goodbye, Daddy. Goodbye... everything.

We drive past the turn to my school, where the nurse had shared her peanut butter crackers with me. Where Mrs. Young had given me a birthday with cupcakes, bought me my first book and fixed me all up when I had an accident.

Where Sharon may have finally wanted to be my friend.

My whole world and everything I've ever known is gone. Derek took it all away from me. Daddy said I could stay with him forever. He promised. *He promised.*

He lied.

I look at Curtis to make sure he's okay. He has his head on my shoulder, holding onto me tight. I worry about one of his arms, which is sandwiched between me and the back of the seat. When I try to pull it out from behind me, he pushes it back and holds onto me tighter.

On the other side of Curtis, I see the two garbage bags; one is on the seat, and the other on the floor. I stare at them.

It's my clothes in there. My shoes. My toothbrush. Anything to do with me is in there. That's *me* inside that garbage bag. Mother had me throw *myself* in a garbage bag, and there it sits, my *whole life* inside it.

A garbage bag.

Curtis and I have been thrown away, just like the trash.

I look up in time to watch us pass the church. I remember the day I'd gotten on the blue bus with Dave and Miss Sandy. I remember when I'd first seen the picture of Jesus on the wall in Sunday school and how the Sunday school teacher had told me Jesus loves me.

Goodbye, blue bus. Goodbye, Dave and Miss Sandy. Goodbye, Pastor Scott, Miss Lisa, and all my new friends. Goodbye, pink slippers.

I close my eyes and rest my head on the back seat as I hold onto Curtis.

Derek.

He told me I was a foster child after he hurt me, And I didn't ask him what it meant.

Now I know.

A single tear slides down my cheek.

It means you do not have a Mommy or Daddy who love you. It means you have no family. You have no one. That is what it means to be a foster child, someone with no one that is trash.

"Jesus, please… please don't leave me too. Amen."

Daddy and Dolly

Meet The Lady Who Survived
Dr. Sharon Zaffarese-Dippold

Dr. Sharon Zaffarese-Dippold lives in Saint Mary's, Pennsylvania, with her husband, Mark, a principal for Brockway Area School District in Brockway, Pennsylvania. She has two children. Her son Joseph is currently serving in the Army with the military police and is married to Elizabeth Zaffarese. They have two children together named Tiberius and Zeta. Dr. Dippold's daughter Jessica is a youth worship leader at "His Tabernacle" church in Ithaca, NY, and she is married to Jason Tubbs, who operates his own tree service business. They have two sons named Elijah and Enoch. Dr. Dippold adores her children and grandchildren.

During Dr. Dippold's childhood years, she lived in foster care. Her experience consisted of multiple foster care and family placement moves involving all forms of childhood abuse and trauma. Dr. Dippold attended approximately ten or more schools during her formative years as she moved from place to place. Her vast school memories consist of academic struggles and bullying in her younger years. From those bullied experiences, Dr. Dippold created a bullying program titled "INAM- It's not about me," A bullying program that she presents in the school systems to deflect the impact of being bullied on children.

Dr. Dippold is also a public speaker and trainer on foster care topics related to her story about growing up in the foster care system. She spoke at the National Child Welfare Leaguer in Radford, Virginia in 2003 and many Child Welfare Agencies regarding her passion about agencies replacing the use of garbage bags with luggage for all foster children moving within the foster care system.

Dr. Sharon Zaffarese-Dippold received a bachelor's degree in Social Work from Mansfield University in 1992 and a master's degree in Social Work from Marywood College in 1995. Her Master Thesis focused on exploring HIV-positive born infants "washing out" from the virus by 15 months of age.

Dr. Sharon Zaffarese-Dippold
Melissa Mulhollan

Dr. Dippold acquired her Ph.D. in Human Services in 2017 from Capella University with a concentration in Human Behavior/Counseling Studies. Her Doctoral Dissertation was published in 2016, *The Lived Experience Of Former Foster Children Who Had to Move Their Belongings In Garbage Bags* October 2016. The Study explored a deeper understanding of the lived experience of 10 women who packed with garbage bags to move while living in foster care. The women ranged in age from 24 to 55 and lived all over the United States. The women shared their stories of packing with garbage bags to move while living in foster care with Dr. Dippold. It was the first time the phenomenon of packing with garbage bags while living in foster care was explored scholarly.

Dr. Sharon Zaffarese-Dippold has a private psychotherapy practice in Pennsylvania. She provides treatment to individuals as young as three years old, couples and families. She treats all mental health symptoms and has practiced for the past twenty-plus years.

Her professional roles have consisted of—

Director of Specialized Foster Care Agency in Radford, VA; Program Director- Foster Care Agency for Catholic Charities in Roanoke. VA; Program Director- of Specialized Foster Care Agency Best Nest Inc in Philadelphia, PA; Program Director- REACH Specialized Foster Care Agency Pathways Inc- in Corning, NY; Program Director- Day Treatment Program- Pathways Inc. Corning, NY; Clinical Social Work Consultant- Glove House Inc Elmira, NY; Program Director- Drug & Alcohol Program- Trinity Elmira, NY; Psychotherapist Contractor- Clinical Associates- in Corning NY.

Dr. Dippold is a published scholar, motivational speaker, and trainer on bullying and foster care topics. She is now authoring her foster care story.

Meet Melissa Mulhollan

Mrs. Melissa Mulhollan lives in DuBois, Pennsylvania with her husband Brian and her son Matthew. Her daughter is currently enrolled for nurse anesthesia at Duke University. Her son is a senior in high school preparing to begin at WVU in the fall of 2022 pursuing a degree in business & finance. Her husband is a principal for Brockway Area School District in Brockway, Pennsylvania. Melissa grew up in Meadville, Pennsylvania and is the daughter of Mr. Glen L. Thompson and Mrs. Carol Thompson, both of Meadville.

Melissa earned her Bachelor of Science degree in secondary education from Clarion University of Pennsylvania in 1991 and has been teaching English at Jefferson County DuBois Area Vocational Technical School since January of 1992. Melissa earned her master equivalency in education in 1993. Melissa also received her certification in life coaching from Life Coaching and Beyond, LLC. in August of 2014.

Melissa received the honor of *"Teacher of the Year"* in the 2016-2017 school year. She served on her school's Building Leadership team for seven years and spearheaded many initiatives. Melissa is a leader and member of multiple committees at her school. Half of her career has been spent as an officer in her local union serving two years as secretary, eight years as vice president and five years as president. She is the first female union president in the school's history since opening its doors in 1969. She is actively giving back to her community as a volunteer.

She published her book, *The Coaching Classroom,* in October 2020. This book is about the success Melissa had incorporating life coaching techniques in the classroom setting to raise student self-worth and academic achievement. She is currently working on curriculum that corresponds with *The Coaching Classroom* called Foundations for Life. This curriculum will be available from CTE Global Publishing in the near future.

For information on speaking engagements, trainings, and presentations with Dr. Sharon Zaffarese-Dippold

Visit: www.DippoldBooks.com
Contact: DrSharon@DippoldBooks.com

Printed in Great Britain
by Amazon

39192414R00136